WORDS PHRASES CLAUSES

WORDS PHRASES CLAUSES

Exercises in English Grammar

THIRD EDITION

REVISED

Edward J. Fox, Jr.
Headmaster Emeritus
Charlotte Latin School

Malcolm T. Moore
formerly of
The Woodbury Forest School

Wayside Publishing

11 Jan Sebastian Dr.
Suite 5
Sandwich, MA 02563

wayside@sprintmail.com
http://www.waysidepublishing.com

ISBN 1-877653-45-4

FOREWORD

In teaching grammar to many students for the past half-century, collectively, we have found that there are certain areas in which many students need additional work. The exercises in this third edition of Words, Phrases, Clauses both touch on the use of words in sentences and concentrate on the use of dependent clauses and verbal phrases in sentences. This new edition also includes exercises on problems related to clauses and phrases, such as the punctuation of clauses and phrases and the case of pronouns.

This textbook was written:
    to help students master clauses and phrases.
    to illustrate patterns useful for learning clauses and phrases.
    to supplement grammar texts that have an insufficient number of sentences.
    to provide more thoughtful and interesting exercises than one usually finds.
    to teach through rule, not through exception.

We have found this book to be most useful:
    as a basal text.
    as a supplementary text in teaching students at any grade level who have continuing difficulty with clauses and phrases.
    as a summer school review.
    as a sole grammar text for many classrooms.

For the most effective use of this book, we recommend:
    that the student follow all instructions and answer all questions.
    that the student read each sentence in a thoughtful manner.
    that the student try to discover the patterns of usage for clauses and verbals.
    that the instructor write additional instructions to further utilize the sentences in the book.

We have kept in mind that the mastery of clauses and phrases is not an end in itself, but only a means to more effective writing on the student's part. We hope that these exercises will aid students in organizing their knowledge and use of English grammar.

We would like to thank the many students, colleagues, friends, and family for their continued help through the years.

We hope that you will enjoy the sentences in this book and the experience of using it.

The Authors

TABLE OF CONTENTS

WORDS

Parts of Speech 2
The Subject 4
The Predicate 8
The Subjective Complement 12
The Direct Object 16
The Indirect Object 20
The Objective Complement 22
The Appositive 24
Modifiers: The Adjective 26
Modifiers: The Adverb 30
Connectors: The Preposition 34
Connectors: The Conjunction 36
The Interjection 38
Test: Parts of Speech Questions 40

CLAUSES

The Noun Clause 42
The Adjective Clause 50
The Adverb Clause 58
Quizzes: Clause Identifications 66
Test: Clause Identifications 70
Test: Clause Constructions 71
Test: Clause Questions 72

PHRASES

The Prepositional Phrase 74
The Gerund and the Gerund Phrase 78
The Participle and the Participial Phrase 88
The Infinitive and the Infinitive Phrase 96
Quizzes: Phrase Identifications 105
Test: Phrase Identifications 109
Test: Phrase Constructions 110
Test: Phrase Questions 111
Final Exercise: The Classical Quiz 112

PROBLEMS

Problems 114
Case of Pronouns 115
Non-Essential (Non-Restrictive) Adjective and Adverb Clauses 116
Introductory Adverb Clauses 117
Introductory Verbals 118
Test: Problems with Verbals and Clauses 119
Mixed Test: Problems with Verbals and Clauses 120

WORDS
WORDS
WORDS
WORDS
WORDS
WORDS
WORDS
WORDS
WORDS
WORDS
WORDS
WORDS
WORDS
WORDS
WORDS
WORDS
WORDS
WORDS

People, especially English-speaking people, are fond of classifying everything. They even like to classify words, phrases, and clauses both as parts of speech and according to their grammatical usage. In turn, the words, phrases, clauses as parts of speech also have a function: that is, they may name, they may predicate, they may modify, they may connect, or they may exclaim.

1. Name the eight parts of speech.

   _____   _____   _____

   _____   _____   _____

   _____   _____

2. What is the function of each part of speech?

3. What is the grammatical usage of each part of speech?

4. May any word, phrase, or clause be a part of speech unless it is used in a sentence?

5. May all sentences be divided into words, phrases, and clauses?

6. Ultimately, may all sentences be divided into words?

7. May all sentences be divided into parts of speech?

8. May all words, phrases, and clauses in a sentence be labeled according to part of speech and according to its grammatical usage?

Parts of Speech	Function	Grammatical Usage
1. Nouns	name	*to name (as subject, subjective complement, direct object, indirect object, objective complement, object of a preposition, appositive, object of a verbal)*
2. Pronouns	name	*to name (as subject, subjective complement, direct object, indirect object, objective complement, object of a preposition, appositive, object of a verbal)*
3. Verbs	predicate	*to predicate (as verbs or verb phrases)*
4. Adjectives	modify	*to modify nouns and pronouns*
5. Adverbs	modify	*to modify verbs, adjectives, and adverbs*
6. Prepositions	connect	*to connect their objects to other words*
7. Conjunctions	connect	*to connect words to words, phrases to phrases, and clauses to clauses*
8. Interjections	exclaim	*to show surprise, mild emotion, or feeling*

1. What is a simple subject of a sentence?

2. What is a complete subject of a sentence?

3. May a simple subject be compound?

4. May a simple subject be modified?

5. Where may a simple subject come in a sentence?

6. What is inverted order?

7. May a subject be understood?

8. May a noun of address or a pronoun of address be a subject?

9. May an object of a preposition be a subject?

10. May the word *there* be a subject?

Underline each <u>simple</u> <u>subject</u> once.

1. <u>Dynasties</u> fall.
2. Young <u>puppies</u> eat noisily.

* * * * *

3. <u>Boys</u> and <u>girls</u> study.
4. Old books and old friends wear well.

* * * * *

5. The <u>man</u> in the moon smiled.
6. An old red barn on the hill burned to the ground.

* * * * *

7. Has the <u>rain</u> ceased?
8. Will the brass gong ring again?

* * * * *

9. Silently flowed the <u>Thames</u>.
10. Quickly through the brush darted the snake.

* * * * *

11. Study. (<u>**You</u> understood**)
12. Go immediately.

* * * * *

13. May <u>I</u> leave, Sir?
14. Did the package arrive, Mrs. Palmer?

* * * * *

15. There goes a good <u>lad</u>.
16. There are many rules in grammar.

* * * * *

17. <u>Hurdlers</u> run and jump.
18. The sun rises in the East and sets in the West.

* * * * *

19. The <u>miser</u> is counting his money.
20. The paintings of Cézanne are valued highly.

* * * * *

21. Enemy <u>forces</u> had been seen on the beach.
22. The winner of the match should have been the young Australian.

* * * * *

23. <u>Stevenson</u> could have been elected.
24. The Ancient Mariner's tale should have been told to everyone.

* * * * *

25. Should the bucking <u>broncos</u> and the Brahma <u>bulls</u> paw the earth and kick their stalls?
26. Could the farmer and his wife milk the cows and churn the butter by sun-up?

Underline each <u>simple</u> <u>subject</u> once.

1. I see your point.
2. I saw *Woodstock* four times.
3. I have seen *Hair* once before.
4. Brent has been seen frequently in study hall.
5. Peter had been seen climbing rocks before the rockslide.

* * * * *

6. Go.
7. Go and never darken my door again!
8. Stop that idiotic behavior!
9. You, Sir, stop that idiotic behavior!
10. Please don't rock the boat.

* * * * *

11. Did you study your vocabulary?
12. Have you learned all the words?
13. Has the ship been sighted by the lookout?
14. Were any freighters sunk by the submarine?
15. Could any of the ships have been lost in the fog?

* * * * *

16. Men, women, and dogs ran through the formal garden.
17. *Men, Women, and Dogs* is the title of one of Mr. Thurber's books.
18. Sinclair Lewis, Ernest Hemingway, William Faulkner, and John Steinbeck have all won the Nobel Prize in literature.
19. The cries of revolution and the sounds of firearms reverberated throughout the plaza.
20. Down the corridors of history echo the footsteps of giants.

* * * * *

21. A person's handwriting can be revealing.
22. The handwriting of a person can contain clues to his personality.
23. Could graffiti be called the handwriting on the wall?
24. The hand is writing without conscious thought.
25. Words, phrases, and clauses can all be subjects of sentences.

26. I am the captain of my fate.
27. You are the apple of my eye.
28. He is the dunce of the class.
29. We are the leaders of the pack.
30. They are the Top Ten records of the month.

* * * * *

31. Daffodils grow.
32. Beautiful daffodils grow.
33. Daffodils and crocuses grow.
34. Yellow daffodils and purple crocuses grow.
35. On the hill by our house beautiful yellow daffodils and colorful purple crocuses grow.

* * * * *

36. The daffodils by my house bloomed last week.
37. The daffodils by my house and the crocuses by the gate bloomed last week.
38. The beautiful yellow daffodils across the road from my house and the colorful purple crocuses by the fish pond bloomed for over two weeks.
39. Did the daffodils bloom?
40. Did the daffodils and crocuses bloom?

* * * * *

41. Endlessly tolled the chapel bells.
42. Over the goalpost once again sailed the ball.
43. Slowly the riverboat gambler turned over his last card.
44. The pen and the sword attacked the enemy in their diverse ways.
45. Came the dawn and the roll of the drums.

* * * * *

46. "Chicago" and "Blood, Sweat, and Tears" use horns in their arrangements.
47. The 1960's were a time of social ferment in America.
48. Both the director and the cameraman screamed in frustration at the startled starlet.
49. *Go, went,* and *gone* are the principal parts of the verb *go.*
50. Colloquialisms, cant, jargon, slang, and vulgarisms have absolutely no place in formal writing.

1. What is a simple predicate of a sentence?

2. What is a complete predicate of a sentence?

3. May a simple predicate be compound?

4. May a simple predicate be modified?

5. What is a helping verb?

6. What is a verb phrase?

7. May a verb phrase contain as many as four verbs?

8. May the parts of a verb phrase be separated by other words?

9. Where may a verb phrase come in the sentence?

Underline each <u>simple</u> <u>predicate</u> twice.

1. Archeopteryxes <u>fly</u>.
2. Joggers jiggle.
3. Lovers leaped.
4. Skaters waltz.
5. Foxes trot.

* * * * *

6. The Urubamba <u>leads</u> to Uilcapampa
7. Chlorophyll is the green in plants.
8. The wheat undulated in the wind.
9. The boxer pulverized Rocky.
10. Wayside Publishing publishes this book.

* * * * *

11. Joanna <u>had</u> <u>dazzled</u> him.
12. Sometimes clothespins do hold noses.
13. Homework sometimes does work hardship.
14. A hard ship will sink.
15. Dromedaries must like camels.

* * * * *

16. David <u>had</u> <u>cut</u> his curly hair.
17. Kind Mr. Martin was enjoying the student's plight.
18. The pyloric sphincter does grind spasmodically.
19. Merry Midas may make many mufflers.
20. She shall sell sea shells.

* * * * *

21. Hank <u>has</u> <u>been</u> <u>hitting</u> home runs.
22. The principal will have said it all.
23. Alice has been volunteered as Costume Chairman.
24. A small gift could have meant a great deal.
25. The guilty man had been tried by his peers.

Underline each <u>simple</u> <u>predicate</u> twice.

1. Dick came.
2. Spot jumped.
3. Jane ran.
4. Jerry saw.
5. Alice looked.

* * * * *

6. Spot ran.
7. Spot was not colorfast.
8. Dick spotted Jane.
9. Jane ran fast.
10. Jane was not colorfast, either.

* * * * *

11. Jerry saw Alice.
12. Alice shrank.
13. Alice was not Sanforized.
14. Mrs. Kilpatrick taught us beautifully.
15. The camel threaded his way into the needle.

* * * * *

16. May I see him now, please?
17. Will you stop that!
18. I am losing my mind!
19. The soccer ball was kicked by Pele.
20. A bar tender was sought by the toothless termite.

* * * * *

21. José could not see the dawn's early light.
22. Poinsettias were named after Joel Poinsett.
23. Workers must increase production.
24. Cars should run on olive oil.
25. Candy manufacturers were switching to artificial sweeteners.

26. The Black Knight shuffled to his feet.
27. Chrysanthemums bloom in the fall.
28. The workman in the bell tower dropped his hammer.
29. Roger Bannister ran the first mile in less than four minutes.
30. The organization restoring the old house is the Ladies Auxiliary of the Hemlock Chowder and Marching Society.

* * * * *

31. *Bang the Drum Slowly* became the most popular book in our library.
32. Through the woods raced the wild stallion.
33. There are many excellent foreign films in town this week.
34. Mr. Beauchamp, cease your caddish behavior!
35. Stop.

* * * * *

36. I may arrive in time for breakfast.
37. The secret agent did not readily divulge his information.
38. The old professor was struck by flying brickbats.
39. Do the movies on television really tell the true story of the old West?
40. Have you really become a fuzz, Mr. Peach?

* * * * *

41. The textbooks probably have not been changed in the last forty years.
42. The young intellectual had been shouting her ideas for most of the evening.
43. The champion should never have fought the overrated challenger.
44. She cannot have told you that!
45. Has the Confederate detachment been moved across the river and into the trees?

* * * * *

46. The precocious children might have been playing with my chemistry set.
47. The meet should never have been won by the Cobras.
48. His behavior would seldom have been tolerated in our day.
49. Boys will be boys; some will be men.
50. The College Board examinations were held in the cafeteria and were attended by over two hundred students.

1. What is a complement?

2. What is a linking verb?

3. What is a predicate noun or pronoun?

4. What is a predicate adjective?

5. May either a predicate noun (pronoun) or a predicate adjective be used as a subjective complement?

6. What two parts of speech may be used as predicate nouns (or pronouns)?

7. What part of speech may be used as a predicate adjective?

8. May a linking verb, by definition, be followed by any grammatical usage other than a subjective complement?

9. List eight verbs other than the verb *to be* which may be used as linking verbs.

    _____   _____

    _____   _____

    _____   _____

    _____   _____

10. What is a subjective complement?

Underline each subjective complement with a dashed line.

. . . as nouns and pronouns

1. This house is a <u>mess</u>!
2. The captain remained a captain.
3. She became chair.
4. Was that he?
5. That was he.

* * * * *

6. Sandpaper feels <u>rough</u>.
7. Sandpipers feel soft.
8. He grew insensitive.
9. He became boorish.
10. The market is bearish.

. . . as adjectives

11. The market should become <u>bullish</u>.
12. Bulls sound bullish.
13. Honey tastes sweet.
14. Quicksand appears firm.
15. Quicksand is mushy.

* * * * *

16. Love stories are <u>mushy</u>.
17. That wave looks swell.
18. Appearances may be deceptive.
19. His appearance seemed ludicrous.
20. Temple always appeared happy.

* * * * *

21. A rose smells <u>sweet</u>.
22. The game was easy.
23. She looked good.
24. He could be happy.
25. The newspaper was red.

Underline each subjective complement with a dashed line.

. . . as nouns and pronouns

1. A. Lincoln was a President.
2. That is she.
3. God is Love.
4. That man was a commando.
5. Stravinsky is a genius.

. . . as adjectives

6. The squad was tired.
7. The children were very happy.
8. Birds smell foul.
9. Candy is dandy.
10. His behavior seemed odd.

* * * * *

11. John was secretary of last year's senior class.
12. Pavlova appeared tired after the long rehearsal.
13. Mr. Kruschev had been premier for a long time.
14. The high Andean air seemed strange to the climber.
15. The people in the photograph are Osa and Martin Johnson.

* * * * *

16. Some teachers are cautious and suspicious.
17. Moby Dick was Captain Ahab's nemesis.
18. Ezra Pound's poetry is both obscure and pedantic.
19. The formal garden was a maze of boxwood.
20. Our basketball center is quite tall this year.

* * * * *

21. After a liberal education on the continent, Lincoln Steffens became a reporter for a New York paper.
22. The lady felt faint, and she grew ill at the thought of raw oysters.
23. Eligibility rules can be a menace to some athletes and coaches.
24. Captain Queeg looked frightened and distraught, and he grew very impatient during the cross-examination.
25. Green persimmons taste awful to green opossums.

26. Winnie the Pooh is my friend.
27. Mighty Mouse is a rat.
28. The test was easy.
29. This history exam will be hard.
30. Will the history exam be hard?

* * * * *

31. The first moon landing was a giant step for mankind.
32. Television serials are mind-boggling.
33. Filmmaking can be an expensive avocation.
34. Beach candy is sandy.
35. The Tower of Babel might be a good name for the United Nations Building.

* * * * *

36. Jefferson became a deist.
37. The pie-eating contestants felt ill.
38. The editorial seemed biased and unfair.
39. To many urban dwellers country living looks ideal.
40. The coconut custard pie tasted too sweet.

* * * * *

41. Can the world be a better place for mankind?
42. "A rose is a rose ...."
43. Miss Chaplin is beautiful.
44. Miss Chaplin is a beautiful girl.
45. Could Miss Chaplin ever become a professional dancer?

* * * * *

46. Push-ups are easy during space-travel.
47. The examination looked easy to the student.
48. Shoplifters are dumb.
49. Television is the Sahara of entertainment.
50. Subjective complements can be words, phrases, or clauses.

1. What is a direct object?

2. What two parts of speech may be used as direct objects?

3. May direct objects be compound?

4. May direct objects be modified?

5. May a direct object ever follow a linking verb?

Circle each direct object.

1. We had a quiz.
2. Then we had a test.
3. I made "100".
4. Four sides can make a rectangle.
5. Peyton liked *Wordly Wise*.

* * * * *

6. John loves Mary.
7. Mary loves Sam.
8. John does not like Sam.
9. The warden anticipated a riot.
10. Tarzan washed his loin cloth.

* * * * *

11. George and Edward were playing games.
12. In Montreal we rode the Metro.
13. They danced a dance.
14. He wrote his composition.
15. Bonnie and John own a station wagon.

* * * * *

16. The Dalmatian chased the fire engine.
17. Light a candle.
18. The telephone company does a good job.
19. The job company has a good telephone.
20. Sophocles used stichomythia.

* * * * *

21. He took umbrage.
22. Turn that water off!
23. Would you peel a grape for me?
24. Thrice we have authored this book.
25. Stone walls do not a prison make.

Circle each ⟨direct object.⟩

1. I love Paris in the springtime.
2. The flanker intercepted the pass.
3. The film disappointed the girl and her date.
4. Giant squids do not like sperm whales.
5. Sperm whales don't like anything.

* * * * *

6. Jim Hawkins sighted Treasure Island.
7. Did Jim Hawkins sight Treasure Island?
8. The guards at the museum eyed the first grade class uneasily.
9. Were the museum guards watching the rowdy children or admiring the pretty teacher?
10. Hold your horses!

* * * * *

11. Please turn the music down.
12. What did you say to the guitar player?
13. What did he tell you?
14. He said that?
15. The hunter watched the covey of quail rise and didn't fire a shot.

* * * * *

16. You can always tell a Harvard man.
17. Yale makes fine locks.
18. Shakespeare wrote 153 sonnets in a modified form of the Petrarchan Sonnet.
19. John Berryman wrote 150 sonnets about a girlfriend of his.
20. Where have all the flowers gone?

* * * * *

21. The student found the direct object in the sentence.
22. He circled the word.
23. Jack Kerouac wrote *On the Road* in six weeks.
24. The lecturer cited an article in last week's *New York Times*.
25. Direct objects naturally follow indirect objects.

26. We study grammar.
27. The jumper cleared the bar.
28. Most students read *Great Expectations*.
29. The irate teacher caned the boy.
30. Have you ever studied music?

* * * * *

31. Stop that infernal racket.
32. The boy copied his lengthy assignment.
33. Automobiles are changing our behavior patterns.
34. Why have you done this despicable deed?
35. Did Dr. Watson ever use Holmes' methods?

* * * * *

36. The drama group presented *The Valiant* in the spring festival.
37. Give the results of the track meet to the sports editor.
38. The Impressionist painters violently disliked the technique of the Romanticists.
39. The British people displayed unmatched courage in the early years of the war.
40. The boys and the girls were preparing the grounds for May Day.

* * * * *

41. Poe wrote one novel and many short stories.
42. The quarterback kept the ball on the next play and then handed it to the defensive right guard by mistake.
43. The ravens were feeding Elijah.
44. Adolph was hanging paper, and he was humming "*Deutschland Uber Alles*."
45. He taught the students well that day, but he did toss one heckler out of the class.

* * * * *

46. These girls are studying English and history, but they are neglecting their athletics.
47. The publishers at 10 Bouverie Street have raised the price of *Punch* to one shilling.
48. In the darkness of the cave Tom Sawyer held Becky Thatcher's hand.
49. All of the boys in the seventh grade have read *Tom Sawyer*, but only a few of them have completed all of their outside reading.
50. The editor-in-chief of the literary magazine parodied "The Raven" for the February issue.

1. What is an indirect object?

2. What two parts of speech may be used as indirect objects?

3. May indirect objects be compound?

4. May indirect objects be modified?

5. May a sentence without a direct object ever contain an indirect object?

6. Does a sentence with a direct object have to contain an indirect object?

Enclose each [indirect object] in brackets.

1. The coach threw [me] the ball.
2. The gendarme asked the lady my name.
3. The vendor sold us some peanuts.
4. Mr. Van Gogh lent Mr. Gauguin five sunflower seeds.
5. An old veteran told us the story of the surrender at Appomattox.

* * * * *

6. Don't give your [baby] or your [parakeet] any eggnog or fruitcake.
7. The clerk of the course gave the coach and the sprinter a final warning.
8. We sent Mr. Alsop a letter of protest.
9. Give the sports editor the results of the meet.
10. The dying Yankee soldier handed Henry the regimental colors.

* * * * *

11. The instructor gave my critical comments due consideration, but he also gave [me] a failing grade.
12. The extra credit questions on the English test concerned Polyphemus and Circe; both had caused Odysseus a great deal of woe.
13. The Board of Visitors gave William Faulkner the opportunity to be writer-in-residence; they also gave the Virginia students an opportunity to know Mr. Faulkner.
14. Shylock lent the merchant 3000 ducats at a costly interest rate.
15. The aging actor gave the final performance every bit of his skill and learning.

* * * * *

16. The librarian lent [me] the book after much persuasion.
17. Capt. Joshua Slocum gave the hull a fresh coat of paint.
18. The little horse gave his harness bells a shake.
19. After the game, we presented the coach the game ball.
20. Give me a sensible answer, or don't tell me anything.

* * * * *

21. The Thought Police gave poor [Winston Smith] a thorough interrogation.
22. The Boy Scout made us a fire by rubbing sticks together.
23. We sent the people in the mission clothing and books.
24. After the long, hot summer the cooling rains in autumn gave the people relief.
25. "Give me liberty, or give me death!"

1   What is a complement?

2.   What is a subjective complement?

3.   What relationship would an objective complement have to the direct object?

4.   May an objective complement be a noun or a pronoun?

5.   May an objective complement be an adjective?

6.   Should the objective complement come after the direct object?

7.   May a sentence without a direct object ever contain an objective complement?

8.   Does a sentence with a direct object have to contain an objective complement?

9.   What is an objective complement?

Enclose each objective complement in a box.

1. The farmer painted the barn red.

2. Rob cut the grass too short.

3. We thought that man good.

4. The employer believed the employee incompetent.

5. The Boss did consider the knights weak.

* * * * *

6. Citizens elected Mr. Johnson President.

7. The squad chose Tiny Tim captain.

8. Henry believed himself a coward.

9. The scholar supposed *The Merchant of Venice* a tragi-comedy.

10. Holden Caulfield made too many people scapegoats.

* * * * *

11. Call me Ishmael.

12. The judges selected that flower prettiest.

13. His class voted Tom the boy most likely to succeed.

14. The teacher believes each student superior.

15. What did they call the baby?

1. May an appositive be a noun?

2. May an appositive be a word, a phrase, or a clause?

3. Does the appositive always come after the noun or pronoun that it re-names?

4. Why are some appositives set off by commas?

5. What is an appositive?

Enclose each (appositive) in parentheses

1. My friend (Flicka) is a horse.
2. Flicka, my friend, is a horse.
3. Our neighbors, the Pitts, are at home.
4. Have you heard Moby Dick and the Wailers, a rock group?
5. He received his birthday present, a new XK-E.

* * * * *

6. Mr. Magoo, a cartoon (character), received a write-in vote.
7. Woodrow Wilson's dream, The League of Nations, was never fully realized.
8. Adam Smith's great book, *The Wealth of Nations*, is read by all economists.
9. My brother Bill has two heads.
10. We girls must leave at once.

* * * * *

11. Our pride and joy, a bouncing baby (boy), will not let us sleep.
12. *The Song of Roland*, a French epic of a legendary hero, dates back from the time of Charlemagne.
13. John, a despised and tyrannical king, was forced into a contract with his knights.
14. There were three great Roman Stoics: Epictetus, Seneca, and Marcus Aurelius.
15. Our school, a good school academically and athletically, is located on a hundred and twenty-two-acre campus.

* * * * *

16. Her hobby, (studying) languages of seven countries, has always fascinated me.
17. I couldn't stand his job, teaching arithmetic to geniuses.
18. Babbitt's preoccupation, conforming to middle class standards, caused his downfall as a man.
19. His chief goal, becoming a success, seemed very remote.
20. The ants' fondest wish, picnicking on a checkered tablecloth, upset the Flower People.

1. What does the word *modify* mean?

2. May an adjective modify a noun or a pronoun?

3. May an adjective come before the noun or pronoun it modifies?

4. May an adjective come after the noun or pronoun it modifies?

5. May an adjective come after the linking verb and modify the subject of the linking verb?

6. What is an adjective?

Circle each adjective other than *a*, *an*, or *the*.
Draw an arrow from each adjective to the word the adjective modifies. Some sentences contain two adjectives.

1. A *blue* marlin is a *large* fish.
2. The modern painting caused critical comments.
3. A family man is a happy man.
4. Brown was an obnoxious fellow.

* * * * *

5. *Five* boys composed the *two* teams.
6. Some cooks use many recipes.
7. One girl had consumed thirteen marshmallows.
8. Many people are called, but few are chosen.

* * * * *

9. The *young* lady carried the *figurative* torch.
10. We saw the Wyoming mountains.
11. He sold Zoysia grass.
12. The Sherman tank rumbled toward the stronghold.

* * * * *

13. *This* book is read by many; *that* book had been read by everyone.
14. These times try the souls of men, but so did those times.
15. Which girl did that?
16. What town will be built on the site?

* * * * *

17. *Whose* book is this?
18. What manner of creature is the Hulk?
19. Tom Brown could explain his actions.
20. Paul's pen wrote in italics.

* * * * *

21. Does your father know the President?
22. He has the dog's leash.

Circle each adjective other than *a*, *an*, or *the*.
Draw an arrow from each adjective to the word the adjective modifies.

1. A green monster went home.
2. The mountain seemed a giant molehill.
3. He kicked the quivering jelly.
4. Peyton rode into the purple sunset.

* * * * *

5. Several men wept together.
6. Laurel and Hardy were two comedians.
7. Moses received Ten Commandments.
8. Grass is eaten by all cows.

* * * * *

9. The Frankish army supported Charlemagne.
10. Ours is the North American continent.
11. Can he fill the Eddie LeBaron shoes?
12. A billy goat collected fees at the troll bridge.

* * * * *

13. This T.V. set turns me on.
14. These are these knees.
15. Those may hold those clothes.
16. Is this the valley of that giant?

* * * * *

17. What kind of fool am I?
18. How many are there?
19. Whose die has been cast?
20. In which bin is the phony?

* * * * *

21. My dog has fleas.
22. Mr. Hyde was Dr. Jekyll's monster.
23. She completed her homework.
24. Lake Buena Vista is in Walt Disney's territory.

25. The white cloud evaporated.
26. The old chair collapsed.
27. Liberated women liberate men.
28. American men need liberation.

* * * * *

29. Happy days are here again.
30. Twenty students signed the protest.
31. Some teachers are tyrants.
32. A few tyrants have been teachers.

* * * * *

33. The Russian poet wrote in English.
34. The Dead Sea Scrolls were a big help to Biblical scholars.
35. Little Orphan Annie's dog is named Sandy.
36. Her benefactor is Daddy Warbucks.

* * * * *

37. Which student drew the caricature?
38. Which of these caricatures did he draw?
39. These are the best drawings of the lot.
40. These drawings demand your attention.

* * * * *

41. North Carolina's Senior Senator was chairman of the committee.
42. The world's tallest building is a city in itself.
43. A growing population will demand rapid transit soon.
44. The 1920's have been called the Jazz Age.

* * * * *

45. The Jolly Roger is the pirate flag.
46. Which artist is the better draftsman?
47. Many students read the controversial novel.
48. Her blue eyes are limpid pools.

1. What does the word *modify* mean?

2. May an adverb modify a verb?

3. May an adverb modify an adjective?

4. May an adverb modify another adverb?

5. May an adverb come before the word that it modifies?

6. May an adverb come after the word that it modifies?

7. What is an adverb?

Circle each adverb.
Draw an arrow from each adverb to the word the adverb modifies. Sentences 5 through 8 each contain two adverbs.

1. He understood now.

2. She was late.

3. Then she knew.

4. Enlightenment could come tomorrow.

* * * * *

5. Superman went up and away.

6. The tide goes in and out.

7. They threw the ball to and fro.

8. Put the books here or there.

* * * * *

9. She had already gone.

10. Do not do that!

11. I was rather good.

12. That joke is so bad.

* * * * *

13. The brown fox jumped quickly.

14. The sleeping dog regarded him lazily.

15. I can easily do that.

16. Edward cleverly performed the magic.

* * * * *

17. The umpire stopped safely.

18. "Amen," he intoned sacredly.

19. "Eat that!" his mother said bitingly.

20. St. George went after the dragon majestically.

Circle each adverb
Draw an arrow from each adverb to the word the adverb modifies.

1. She would seldom waste anything.

2. John was graduated early.

3. That loud-mouth is often a boor.

4. The boy never went.

* * * * *

5. Speed ran home.

6. The confetti was scattered around.

7. Boats drew near.

8. There stands my monument.

* * * * *

9. He batted the ball well.

10. The car has not been used.

11. I thank you muchly.

12. Lord Fauntleroy was too good.

* * * * *

13. He completed the course happily.

14. The baby was eating noisily.

15. Fearfully, the hunter stalked the lion.

16. Fight fiercely, Harvard!

* * * * *

17. The little hound barked doggedly.

18. The wedding guest arose early.

19. He avoided church religiously.

20. Miss Mississippi won the beauty contest swimmingly.

21. We arrived early.

22. We arrived too early.

23. We arrived much too early.

24. We arrived first.

* * * * *

25. Gratefully the writer welcomed his check.

26. The writer gratefully welcomed his check.

27. The writer welcomed his check gratefully.

28. The grateful writer smiles euphorically.

* * * * *

29. Some students write well.

30. Some students write very well.

31. No one ever writes too well.

32. Good writers use grammar correctly.

* * * * *

33. Only recent American novels will be read in senior English next year.

34. Recent American novels only will be read in senior English next year.

35. Recent American novels will be read only in senior English next year.

36. Recent American novels will be read in senior English only next year.

* * * * *

37. Swiftly and silently soared the sailplane.

38. Immediately the alarm sounded shrilly in our ears.

39. The extremely tired runner dropped out of the very demanding race.

40. Use adverbs sparingly.

1. May a preposition consist of more than one word?

2. Does a preposition always have an object?

3. Does a preposition connect its object to another word in the sentence?

4. Does a preposition always have to be a part of the prepositional phrase?

5. May a prepositional phrase be used as an adverbial modifier or an adjective modifier?

6. What is a preposition?

Enclose each (prepositional phrase) in parentheses.
Underline each <u>preposition</u>.

1.   He went (<u>aboard</u> the ship).

2.   The baby crawled about the house.

3.   Dana sailed before the mast.

4.   The miner could walk despite the accident.

5.   Everyone should go with John.

* * * * *

6.   The house (<u>down</u> the block) is haunted.

7.   The course for me is English!

8.   The jack-in-the-box popped up.

9.   The book of the month is read carefully.

10.   Ten minutes past the hour was struck.

* * * * *

11.   (<u>Up</u> the chimney) St. Nicholas rose.

12.   Since that time no one has called him.

13.   Around the rugged rock, the ragged rascal ran.

14.   On the 31st we enplane for Tierra del Fuego.

15.   From the night came eerie sounds.

* * * * *

16.   (<u>Because</u> <u>of</u> the weather) the game was called.

17.   Instead of cake we want bread.

18.   According to Hoyle a person should always play cards.

19.   In spite of the waves the swimmer dashed in.

20.   I am going out of my mind.

1. May a conjunction join a word to a word?

2. May a conjunction join a phrase to a phrase?

3. May a conjunction join a clause to a clause?

4. May a conjunction consist of more than one word?

5. May conjunctions be used in pairs?

6. What is a conjunction?

Enclose each (conjunction) in parentheses.
Underline the <u>words</u>, the <u>phrases</u>, or the
<u>clauses</u> that the conjunction connects.

1. The young boy jumped <u>up</u> (and) <u>down</u>.
2. English or history is my favorite subject.
3. The guests at the house party had been singing and dancing for most of the evening.

* * * * *

4. <u>Washing dishes</u> (and) <u>cleaning house</u> are not my favorite pastimes.
5. I will do my homework or watch the late, late show.
6. We went across the river and into the trees to see General Jackson.

* * * * *

7. <u>Senator Claghorn is very popular</u>, (but) <u>he has a poor attendance record</u>.
8. I never worry about my essays, nor do I worry about the grades.
9. The men assembled in the living room, and the women sat in the parlor, but the children played on the large porch.

* * * * *

10. The baby ate (not only) her <u>squash</u> (but also) her <u>peas</u>.
11. He will get neither supper nor sympathy.
12. We have to see either the carpenter or his helper.

* * * * *

13. The keys are (either) <u>in the car</u> (or) <u>on the desk</u>.
14. Both modeling in clay and carving in stone are aspects of sculpture.
15. The team was determined either to win the game or to die trying.

* * * * *

16. (Not only) <u>were his parents misbehaving</u> (but also) <u>his pets were</u>.
17. Either you go or I will!
18. Not only did the Spaniards try to settle the Mississippi Delta from the south, but also the French came down from the north.

* * * * *

19. <u>The moon seemed to be very far away</u>; (still) <u>our astronauts were undaunted by the distance</u>.
20. Captain Hook fell off the boat; consequently, he was eaten by a hungry crocodile.
21. Cherries may be used for pies; however, they must be pitted first.

1. Does an interjection have any grammatical relationship in a sentence?

2. May an interjection be used to show emotion or feeling?

3. May an interjection be followed by an exclamation point?

4. May an interjection be more than one word?

5. What is an interjection?

Underline each <u>interjection</u>.

1. <u>Eek</u>! There's a mouse!

2. Great Caesar's ghost! I've passed my French.

3. Dear me, I am overwhelmed.

4. Ah, ha! Have I found the vandals at last?

5. Gadzooks!

* * * * *

6. <u>Oh</u>, how can he do that to me?

7. Alas! (sigh) Woe is me!

8. Eureka! I have just found the soap!

9. Tsk, tsk. That's so sad.

10. Zounds! I've been wounded mortally to the death!

1. Name the eight parts of speech.

    _____   _____

    _____   _____

    _____   _____

    _____   _____

2. What is the difference between a part of speech and its grammatical usage?

3. What are the two main parts of a sentence?

4. What two parts of speech are used as subjects?

5. What part of speech is used as the predicate?

6. What is a modifier?

7. What two parts of speech are used as modifiers?

8. What part of speech must always introduce a prepositional phrase?

9. What part of speech is used to connect words to words, phrases to phrases, or clauses to clauses?

10. What part of speech is used to express surprise?

11. What two parts of speech are used as objects?

12. How does a direct object differ from a subjective complement?

CLAUSES
CLAUSES
CLAUSES
CLAUSES
CLAUSES
CLAUSES
CLAUSES
CLAUSES
CLAUSES
CLAUSES
CLAUSES
CLAUSES
CLAUSES
CLAUSES
CLAUSES
CLAUSES
CLAUSES
CLAUSES
CLAUSES

1. What is a noun clause?

2. What kinds of words introduce noun clauses?

3. List some words which may introduce noun clauses.

   _____ _____ _____ _____

   _____ _____ _____ _____

   _____ _____ _____ _____

   _____ _____ _____ _____

4. May the introductory word in a noun clause ever be omitted?

5. List eight ways noun clauses may be used.

   _____ _____ _____ _____

   _____ _____ _____ _____

6. May a noun clause be used every way that a noun may be used?

7. Are there any particular rules of punctuation for noun clauses?

Enclose each (noun clause) in parentheses.

. . . as subject

1. (That he will never be elected president) seems fairly obvious.
2. That noun clauses may be subjects of sentences is easily demonstrated.
3. Why I collect fossils puzzles my friends.
4. Why Steinbeck received the Nobel Prize puzzled Steinbeck.
5. How he solved the complex algebra problem amazed the instructor.

* * * * *

. . . as subjective complement (predicate noun)

6. The fact is (that Santiago is a Christ symbol).
7. The point of the story was that human virtue can be distorted by poverty.
8. The theme of his talk was what we had anticipated.
9. His answer was what I wanted.
10. The lawyer's next question to the plaintiff was why he threw the cherry bombs at his mother-in-law.

* * * * *

. . . as direct object

11. I know (who you are).
12. He sensed what we meant.
13. Many men have wondered whether light rays from the sun are curved.
14. Most athletes know why smoking is harmful.
15. *The New York Times* prints what is fit to print.

* * * * *

. . . as indirect object

16. The doorman gave (whoever had passes) special consideration.
17. The zealous coach gave whomever she saw wheat germ tablets.
18. He will give whatever you say special attention.

* * * * *

. . . as objective complement

19. They nicknamed her (what she wanted to be named).
20. The charming rogue called the attractive young lady what she wanted to be called.
21. The voters would have elected Ike whatever he would have wished in 1952.

. . . as appositive

22. The fact (that she is beautiful) will never be disputed.
23. His implication that I didn't study at all should not be announced to everyone.
24. The saying that a penny saved is a penny earned appealed to the Yankee tradesmen's sense of thrift.

* * * * *

. . . as object of the preposition

25. We'll go at (whatever time you designate).
26. I wrote the note to whomever it concerned.
27. Mosby's Rangers supported themselves with whatever they could forage.
28. The secret society lent its support with whatever funds were available.
29. The village gossip spread the false rumor to whoever passed by.

* * * * *

. . . as object of a verbal

30. The S.M.E.R.S.H. agent liked knowing (what James Bond's diabolical scheme was).
31. To know what one should do in an emergency can be very valuable to anyone.

* * * * *

. . . as subject (after an expletive)

32. It is nice (that you are going).
33. It is natural that boys should behave strangely in the springtime.

* * * * *

. . . as direct object (in a direct quotation)

34. Caesar asked, ("Who are the Celts?")
35. "Graduation is just the beginning," concluded the long-winded speaker.

Enclose each (noun clause) in parentheses.
Tell the grammatical usage of each noun clause.

1. (How young people can listen to the radio all day) is a mystery to me.

2. Whoever tries can paint.

3. Whoever put the guppies in the punch bowl is going to be in trouble.

4. Whatever he did seemed wrong.

5. Whatever books you read this summer will count toward your parallel reading.

* * * * *

6. The amazing enigma was (why Captain Ahab nailed the gold piece to the mast).

7. Aunt Polly's tonic was what Tom Sawyer needed.

8. Your future will partly be what you make it.

9. The daily meeting of his composition class was what he feared most.

10. Her reception was what she deserved.

* * * * *

11. The Declaration of Independence guarantees (that all men are entitled to the pursuit of happiness).

12. My mother said that I can take driving lessons next summer.

13. "There seems to be something in my soup," Tom said grittily.

14. "Do we have an examination tomorrow?" Tom asked testily.

15. "This ginger ale has lost its effervescence," Tom stated flatly.

* * * * *

16. (That he knew his Sanskrit) was apparent.

17. Whoever wears such an outfit should be incarcerated.

18. What this country needs is a good five-cent cigar.

19. Whatever that child does gives her grandfather ulcers.

20. Whoever grabs the brass ring wins a free ride.

21.   Crabby Appleton asked where Badlands Meany was.

22.   One of the King's men reported that the wall was still up.

23.   No one knows how Icarus flew with homemade wings.

24.   The astronaut wondered where the green cheese was.

25.   Geordie said, "Go bridle me my milk-white steed."

* * * * *

26.   His idea is that the faithful should be rewarded.

27.   The gift was what he wanted.

28.   An ideal should not be what is easily attainable.

29.   The final answer was what you would have expected.

30.   The firemen's plan is that the toys be reconditioned by Christmas.

* * * * *

31.   Doofo never studies except what he has to.

32.   Food was given to whoever wished for it.

33.   For what it's worth, ants never sleep.

34.   The gunfighter was driven out of whatever town he entered.

35.   With whichever players are left, you must finish the game.

* * * * *

36.   The fact that he behaved so oddly proved his undoing.

37.   That anyone has hiccoughs is an interesting phenomenon.

38.   The fact is that I should be delighted to go.

39.   She asked whether I could do it.

40.   The gossip told whoever wanted to listen the news.

41. We considered Claghorn what the Democratic Party needed.

42. After what you have asked, I can believe anything.

43. The fact that she won the pole vault in the state meet enabled her to get a scholarship.

44. The academic committee wanted to do what was best.

45. We resented his knowing whom we had planned to visit.

* * * * *

46. Sensing that the building was surrounded, the U.N.C.L.E. agent climbed toward the roof.

47. The Good Humor man gave ice cream to whoever wanted it.

48. I don't believe that he can do it.

49. What she said to me cannot be repeated.

50. Robert Jordan learned to his horror that Pablo had stolen the dynamite.

* * * * *

51. It is obvious that the good guys in western movies wear white hats.

52. Old Mr. McLaughlin said, "Don't go near the water."

53. Old Mr. McLaughlin said that we shouldn't go near the water.

54. He told me she would be glad to write a recommendation to the college.

55. I gave what you told me careful consideration.

* * * * *

56. We told Piggy what we thought he should hear.

57. Whoever thinks about noun clauses will understand them.

58. The coaches always give the award for outstanding player to whoever does the most for the team.

59. The strange thing is that Abercrombie doesn't seem to care about his gross appearance.

60. The fact that Washington actually threw the dollar across the Rappahannock does not really surprise most Americans.

61.   What the troops heard was the sound of the explosion.

62.   The tired old pedagogue said that there was more than one way to analyze the sentence.

63.   I know who you are, where you came from, and what you want.

64.   It is an ironic conception to most of us that the shortest distance between two points in space may be a curved line.

65.   What I can't understand is why he told me.

* * * * *

66.   It was taken for granted that Minnesota Fats would challenge the young stranger to a game of straight pool.

67.   The tone-deaf boy's real reason for going to hear the string quartet was that his girl was going.

68.   "How Puritanism Has Affected American Literature" was the topic of Mr. Norton's lecture.

69.   I'll always disagree in principle with what he says.

70.   The older generation has said for 2500 years that the younger generation is going to the dogs.

* * * * *

71.   A teacher knows instinctively who is interested in his course.

72.   Her belief that education makes for inequality fascinated the faculty.

73.   The little girl asked innocently, "Why does the sun shine in the daytime?"

74.   Benedict pleaded, "Why don't you believe me?"

75.   Stella asked, "Can I really find happiness?"

* * * * *

76.   That he secretly likes reading was a happy discovery.

77.   It was evident that Don had made many mathematical errors.

78.   The farmer worried about how she would catch the kangaroos.

79.   Doofo asked whether he was completely acceptable in polite society.

80.   The fact that the vending machines were empty caused great dismay.

81. The fact that our candidate had been defeated was confirmed by the morning news.

82. The Speaker of the House announced that the motion had been passed by a large majority.

83. The Headmaster was concerned about what his teachers did with their spare time.

84. What has been decided by the students is untenable to the administration.

85. Tom was forced to look continually at whatever the teacher wrote on the blackboard.

* * * * *

86. That his grandmother wore combat boots was known to all of Doofo's peers.

87. The truth is that Bill escaped from the funny farm.

88. That the team had won was known throughout the city.

89. What a dictator does may change the course of history.

90. A person can be whatever he or she wishes.

* * * * *

91. That all students work continually on English is seldom realized by their teachers.

92. The principle to remember is simply that water will not flow uphill.

93. Napoleon found that Russia in the winter was not to his liking.

94. The new queen will be whomever the king chooses.

95. Salome coldly rejected whatever baubles did not please her.

* * * * *

96. That Oedipus murdered his father was the main topic of discussion in Thebes.

97. His financial backers discovered that Marco Polo had not yet returned from his trip.

98. What this country needs is a good five-cent nickel.

99. It will be difficult to believe whoever told you that.

100. He will work for whoever gives him the most interesting job.

1. What is an adjective clause?

2. What is a relative pronoun?

3. List the five relative pronouns that introduce adjective clauses.

   _____   _____   _____

   _____   _____

4. Does the relative pronoun have a grammatical use within the adjective clause?

5. Name two adverbs that may introduce adjective clauses.

   _____   _____

6. May the relative pronoun ever be omitted?

7. Why are some adjective clauses set off by commas?

Enclose each (adjective clause) in parentheses.
Draw an arrow to the word the clause modifies.

1. He is a boy (who studies).

2. A boy who studies will succeed.

3. She is the lady who paints portraits.

4. The lady who paints portraits is a friend of ours.

5. They are the students who will go to the shindig.

* * * * *

6. He is a boy (whom I know).

7. A boy whom I know won a Fulbright Scholarship.

8. This is the lady whom we visited last summer.

9. The lady whom we visited last summer told us about the depression years.

10. They are the students whom you saw last week at the lecture.

* * * * *

11. *Brave New World* is a book (that fascinates me).

12. A book that fascinates me is *Brave New World*.

13. The concept of equality was one idea that we understood.

14. One idea that we understood was the concept of equality.

15. They are the noisy students that you heard last week.

* * * * *

16. This is a place (which frightens me).

17. This is a place which I detest.

18. This is a place from which we can view the entire area.

19. This is the wall-safe in which Commander Whitehead keeps his supply of quinine water and bitter lemon.

20. The floorboards under which good old Silas Marner kept his money were riddled by termites.

51

21. Mr. Bonderchunk is the man (whose land adjoins ours).

22. Mr. Bonderchunk, whose land adjoins ours, is a power-hungry land baron.

23. Picasso is a painter whose work has influenced many Twentieth Century artists.

24. Picasso, whose work has influenced many Twentieth Century artists, is my favorite painter.

25. A woman whose husband sings in the scullery is one whose soul is at peace.

* * * * *

26. Now is the time (when you should think).

27. This is the place where you should think.

28. In 1939, when the World's Fair was held, we had one of the hottest summers ever recorded.

29. In New York, where the World's Fair was held, the temperature soared to record heights.

30. During the Civil War, when tactics in warfare changed radically, many weapons were perfected in the battlefield, where necessity is often the mother of invention.

* * * * *

31. He is a boy (I know).

32. A girl I know won a Honda.

33. The Taj Mahal was the place the Ambassador visited.

34. The place the Ambassador visited was the Taj Mahal.

35. The joke I liked best was the one he told about General DeGaulle and the foreign legionnaire.

Enclose each (adjective clause) in parentheses.
Draw an arrow to the word the clause modifies.

1. People (who live in glass houses) should lower their blinds.

2. Any person who knows me well will understand.

3. A man whom we knew wrote "The Wreck of Old 97."

4. The person whom I questioned was unable to give me directions.

5. Mr. Sebastian Flyte, whom you may never have heard of, used to play with a teddy bear in college.

* * * * *

6. The person with whom you were speaking is the author of the play.

7. Anton Chekhov, whose works we have read, is a great Russian dramatist.

8. Saint Paul, whose conversion some celebrate on January 25, was the topic of the sermon.

9. Shakespeare is a name that most students recognize.

10. Here is another picture that you will surely like.

* * * * *

11. The driver told us about a waterfall which we had never seen.

12. A subscription to *Horizon* was the gift which our class gave to the library.

13. In 1939, when Poland was invaded, I took my first airplane ride.

14. During the middle of the Twentieth Century, when World War III seemed imminent, there was much unrest among the young people in America.

15. She took a trip to Richmond, Virginia, where the state legislature was meeting.

* * * * *

16. My family vacationed in Corticella, Italy, where our forefathers once lived.

17. The meal I like best is chicken curry.

18. The book I read was not on the approved reading list.

19. The street where he lives is lined with giant Dutch elms.

20. The time when I expect you will be very early in the morning.

21. This is a ball that was used in the 1950 World Series.

22. She is the one of whom I was speaking.

23. That can't be the boy whose arm was broken.

24. He had a rare stamp which I wanted.

25. Daddy Warbucks, who always wears a diamond stickpin, represents capitalism.

* * * * *

26. *The Graduate*, which many people have read, is a controversial movie.

27. That automobile, which has dual carburetors, was painted red, white, and blue.

28. I knew a teacher once who sailed alone to Bermuda in a sloop that had only a mainsail.

29. The librarian showed me the section of the library which contained books that might be useful to me.

30. Jesse Owens, whose Olympic records in the broad jump stood for twenty-five years, spoke to the young boys and girls who were interested in track.

* * * * *

31. Now is the hour when all good men should go home.

32. The landlord showed the lady a room where she could write undisturbed.

33. Dante Alighieri, who wrote the *Divine Comedy*, was very much involved in Florentine politics.

34. Here is a boy who will do the work.

35. The smile she gave me was very reassuring.

* * * * *

36. Mr. Mattfield, from whom we learned of the glories of English literature, gave me advice that I have never forgotten.

37. We went to Washington, where the National Gallery is located, in the fall of 1949, when the new Cézannes were shown for the first time.

38. She is the lady whom we saw at the theatre.

39. The team of which I am speaking is in the National League.

40. Geology is offered for those girls whose interest is in earth science.

41. The Bishop is a man who commands respect.

42. Will Rogers never met a person whom he disliked.

43. Van Gogh was one painter whose paint is still wet.

44. This is the foundation of the bridge which collapsed in 1939.

45. Lithography is an art which I am studying.

* * * * *

46. Anthropology seemed to be one subject which he knew nothing about.

47. Mr. Apley gave his son a book which he wanted him to read.

48. There are many rules and practices in cricket that puzzle Americans.

49. Pirates' Alley is an attraction that we visited in New Orleans.

50. Gerry is not the man that he was.

* * * * *

51. David Harum traded the horse that he wished to get rid of.

52. The Fourth Century, B.C.E., was a time when Sparta was the supreme power in the Aegean world.

53. Shadwell, Virginia, is the place where Thomas Jefferson was born.

54. She read and loved many of the poems that e e cummings wrote.

55. Perfection is an ideal which we seldom attain.

* * * * *

56. It was the very car that he had bought an hour before.

57. The pistol which she pointed at the burglar who confronted her was not loaded.

58. The magnificence of the buildings that had been erected in Hindustan amazed even travelers who had seen the splendid dome of St. Peter's.

59. In all of the shops that we visited the two would ask the prices of a lot of articles that they had no idea of buying.

60. A man whose conscience is in good working order will seize every opportunity that is offered to him.

61. That attractive girl whom you met at the game will be at the party tonight.
62. We went to the Redskins-Colts game in an antique car that should have been condemned years ago.
63. Charlie Parker, who with Dizzy Gillespie and Thelonious Monk was the founder of modern jazz, died tragically at an early age.
64. This is a book I like which you'll enjoy.
65. We were required to read *The Sun Also Rises*, in which Hemingway gives us an excellent picture of the "lost generation."

* * * * *

66. In a time when science and medical research have freed man from plagues, pestilence, and many crippling diseases, we still suffer from the common cold.
67. She is a teacher who everyone thought was extremely pedantic but who had a good sense of humor.
68. The place where you put the fishing worms has been discovered by a robin.
69. Old Angus McDougald, who still has the first dollar he ever made, gave a token donation to the fund for the Abolishment of Spending.
70. The poem which Ballantine read to the class shocked Miss Peabody, who promptly sent the hapless boy to the office.

* * * * *

71. Hannah More Academy, which was the oldest Episcopal girls' school in America, was located in Reisterstown, Maryland.
72. Sam, who is fast becoming the "compleat angler," is trying to find a lure for small-mouth bass which will not only entice the fish but completely hypnotize them.
73. What was the time when you were supposed to go home?
74. There are several places in South America where I have always wanted to spend some time.
75. Ask Kilroy, who was there.

* * * * *

76. We all tend to appreciate people who don't talk about themselves continually.
77. Yesterday I had a meal that suited me exactly.
78. I heard something today that made me ponder the universal problem of existence.
79. Santiago appreciated the attention that the boy showed for him.
80. Billy Budd quickly learned about Mr. Claggart, who openly resented him.

81. Any student in this class who wants to receive extra credit must do all of the parallel reading.

82. Is this the same car you had the last time I saw you?

83. Try not to think of things that bother you.

84. She is a person who has a great deal of talent.

85. We stepped up into the bow of the cutter, where the wind blew fiercely.

* * * * *

86. Superman, who entered the small phone booth, could not get his clothes changed.

87. The place where everyone had fun is the Purple Rat-Fink.

88. The palace in which he fiddled burned down.

89. We ran rapidly to windward, where the gale was whipping up the waves.

90. The boy who forgot his copy of *The Oresteian Trilogy* soon forgot about passing English.

* * * * *

91. Romeo was looking for the house where his true love lived.

92. Who is the man who takes the tickets?

93. The students who drove to Ft. Lauderdale soon walked back to college.

94. Tess married the man that played the second-hand harp.

95. The team that controls the ball has the better chance of winning.

* * * * *

96. The person who advances with the changing times will not be left behind.

97. The family that plays together stays together.

98. Please don't give me a home where the buffaloes roam.

99. Anything that she wanted was hers for the asking.

100. The alert officer questioned the integrity of the man whom he suspected.

1. What is an adverb clause?

2. What kind of words introduce adverb clauses?

3. List some subordinate conjunctions.

     _____   _____   _____   _____

     _____   _____   _____   _____

     _____   _____   _____   _____

     _____   _____   _____   _____

4. When is an adverb clause elliptical?

5. Should a comma always come after an introductory adverb clause?

6. Should a comma always set off adverb clauses introduced by the words *as*, *since*, and *for*, when they mean *because*?

**Enclose each (adverb clause) in parentheses.
Draw an arrow to the word the clause modifies.**

because   1.   (Because he was late), he hurried home.

because   2.   He hurried home (because he was late).

if   3.   If you plan your work, you can work your plan.

if   4.   You can work your plan if you plan your work.

when   5.   When it rains, Morton's salt pours.

when   6.   Morton's salt pours when it rains.

after   7.   After the battle was over, the fields of Brandy Station were red.

after   8.   The fields of Brandy Station were red after the battle was over.

whenever   9.   Whenever the jazz combo played, the students went berserk.

whenever   10.   The students went berserk whenever the jazz combo played.

Until   11.   Until he begins to exercise self-discipline, Will will continually be frustrated.

Until   12.   Will will continually be frustrated until be begins to exercise self-discipline.

although   13.   Although he was only four, Sam was a full-time comedian.

although   14.   Sam was a full-time comedian although he was only four.

while   15.   While the fat emperor fiddled, the city burned.

while   16.   The city burned while the fat emperor fiddled.

as   17.   As the symbolism in the book was too obscure, most of the students missed the meaning.

as   18.   Most of the students missed the meaning, as the symbolism in the book was too obscure.

since   19.   Since we did not pick up our tickets, we missed the concert.

since   20.   We missed the concert, since we did not pick up our tickets.

than   21.   He looked stronger (than I did).

than   22.   New York is larger than Chicago.

than   23.   A bird in the hand is better than two in the bush.

than   24.   Spinach tastes worse than broccoli.

than   25.   Greta Garbo is much prettier than Sophia.

* * * * *

that   26.   He studied so hard (that he had a nervous breakdown).

that   27.   The fullback hit me so hard that my chinstrap burst.

that   28.   John Coulter ran so swiftly that the Indians couldn't catch him.

* * * * *

as   29.   She smiled as sweetly (as an angel).

as   30.   She was as cute as a button.

Enclose each (adverb clause) in parentheses.
Draw an arrow to the word the clause modifies.

1. Because he was a wanderer, Ishmael wanted to put to sea.

2. If I were Caesar, then I would act like Caesar.

3. Unless Casey comes to bat soon, the Mudville nine will lose this game.

4. Since I had never seen a moor, I did not know what to expect.

5. While we were traveling in the desert, we became very hot and thirsty.

* * * * *

6. My colleague looked at me as if I were crazy.

7. Rob caught sixteen fish after everyone else had gone home.

8. The little boy ran to his mother when she called.

9. You may stay out until the cows come home.

10. She died as she lived, a woman.

* * * * *

11. My youngest brother is taller than I.

12. Johnny Quest can do anything better than you.

13. That first star in Orion seems brighter than the middle star.

14. Sleepier than most, Endymion was eventually awakened.

15. Faster than I, Jesse could always beat me to the draw.

* * * * *

16. That stubborn mule kicked me so hard that I flew into the air.

17. Bertrand Russell behaved as sprightly as a chicken.

18. That sandpaper is as rough as some ballplayers' beards.

19. My students are really not so much smarter than your students.

20. German is not so difficult as one would imagine.

21. Although she was the rancher's youngest daughter, she knew the ranch business well.

22. The cannibals were much better prepared than the missionaries were.

23. Although the water was quite cold, the scuba diver stayed under the ice until he found the mermaid.

24. I always believed that Icarus, wherever he fell into the ocean, would be found.

25. I waited at the gate so long for Katie that I married her best friend.

* * * * *

26. When the rescuers first discovered the wreck of "Old 97," thousands of canaries were flying around the smoldering ruins.

27. Jane would not go to the dance with the guitar-strumming youth until he got a haircut.

28. Though many are called, few are chosen.

29. Jim Clark's avocado-green Lotus was out of the race before he even got started.

30. Students work harder today than they used to.

* * * * *

31. Prince Edward abdicated so that he could marry a commoner.

32. Although there is plenty of room at the top, most people don't reach the pinnacles of success.

33. Huck and Jim drifted down the river after they were given up for dead.

34. As Mr. Toynbee has told us, civilizations tend to rise, reach a peak, and then decline.

35. "The Louisville Lip" hit Sonny Liston so hard that he floored him with one punch.

* * * * *

36. Would you please send me an application blank so that I might apply for the position?

37. Ulysses crept to the mouth of the cave while the giant Polyphemus slept.

38. Whether you know it or not, you've goofed again.

39. He worked very hard in English because he had a flair for writing.

40. Since *Lord of the Flies* contained so much symbolism, we had no trouble finding theme topics.

41. You may go to the game tonight, provided that you come home early.
42. I foolishly took the dare and swung out over the broiling rapids lest my friends think me "chicken."
43. Minnesota Fats controlled the cue ball as if he were a magician.
44. If everyone had something important to do, he would not have time to gossip.
45. Jim Ryun ran the last 220 yards of the mile as if he was going to break the world's record.

* * * * *

46. Even if he passes Algebra I, he'll still have to go to summer school to take French.
47. Lest you get the wrong idea, I am still captain of the Hemlock Chowder and Marching Society.
48. He pledged undying love till the earth stopped turning on its axis.
49. Unless something is done about inertia and bureaucracy in large corporations, we may soon swamp ourselves in petty details.
50. I am ready to go to Sorrento whenever you are.

* * * * *

51. The Caped Crusader can always be found where the action is.
52. Whither you goest, I will go.
53. As the major powers in Europe and Asia were girding for war, isolationists in America were still talking of non-intervention.
54. The weak student wrote so fast that he broke the point of his pencil.
55. When the roll is called up yonder, I'll be there.

* * * * *

56. In the documentary film about the development of the rocket, many of the missiles blew up before they could be launched.
57. Pamela is a much better student than her brother.
58. We had more rain last summer than we wanted.
59. If you want to see all of the exhibits in the Smithsonian Institute in one day, you must not stay in any place for long.
60. With all of the pomp and circumstance surrounding the old writer, with the accolades and laurels bestowed upon him, after all of the glory and honors given him for his many glorious achievements, he is still lonelier than most people.

61. Since the goalie had sustained a knee injury during pre-season practice, she was unable to participate during the entire field hockey season.

62. Photographer's flashbulbs blinded the candidate as he delivered his speech.

63. As long as there are men, there will be wars.

64. The ship, when it became completely filled with water, sank like a stone.

65. The boys stood on the corner while they watched the girls go by.

* * * * *

66. When the television program is over, Bill will study.

67. Although the television program is over, Bill is not studying.

68. Bill is now studying, as his parents have chased him upstairs.

69. He stayed in the swimming pool until his lips became lavender-blue.

70. The hunter went hunting even though dove season had not opened.

* * * * *

71. Forrest has to practice football, while Peter is running cross-country.

72. If everyone spoke a common language, Babel would probably be rebuilt.

73. Until you succeed in business, you should keep trying.

74. When Doofo sat down, the bench broke; when he got up, he hit his head.

75. We will stay here as long as you.

* * * * *

76. Because the team's behavior was a bit wild, they were not allowed to take any more trips.

77. If the train had not hit him, the chicken thief would still be running down the track.

78. The man was extremely dirty, since he had been working in the grease pit.

79. We did have twenty-five percent fewer teeth, as the survey indicated.

80. Whilst the television audience cheered, Joltin' Jimmy was floored by Mr. Clean.

81. The white knight turned pink when he fell off the horse.

82. Martha slept while George ironed.

83. Jane called for Tarzan, since she was being chased by a mad tiger.

84. When there was no more need for them, the vigilantes returned home.

85. Even though it rains and the sun seldom shines, we enjoy the indoor sports.

* * * * *

86. After the sun goes down, it is dark.

87. I waited until morning came.

88. I left when I should have stayed.

89. I will finish as he did.

90. If you go, so will I.

* * * * *

91. The Middle School girls quickly assembled to watch when the boys appeared on the tennis courts.

92. While in class, I pay attention whenever I should.

93. Although pink elephants don't have sharp toenails, I don't want one to step on me.

94. Because she is an avid reader, she devours books.

95. Since I am his elder, he respects me.

* * * * *

96. He was as old as anyone else.

97. We must go so that others may take our places here.

98. Underdog goes wherever he is needed whenever he is needed.

99. The door squeaked when the wind blew through it.

100. Since we started this text, much water has gone over the dam.

Enclose each (dependent clause) in parentheses.
(Only the most common types of usage of clauses are given here.)

Noun clause as subject

1. That we are beginning anew may occur to you.
2. Whoever wishes can write a grammar text.
3. Whatever publisher will print it will be commended.

Noun clause as subjective complement (predicate noun)

4. The fact is that I am never wrong.
5. Helena's statement was that Montana is wonderful.
6. Perry's summation to the jury was that his client was innocent.

Noun Clause as direct object

7. Velikovsky demonstrates that ancient Egyptian chronology errs.
8. Edward insisted that his was the only way.
9. She stated soundly that she should sell sea-shells by the seashore.

Noun clause as object of the preposition

10. Would Lee grant a wish to whoever came to Appomattox?
11. Give the minimum wage to whoever works the maximum.
12. Under whatever conditions you wish, I want you at this school.

Adjective clause: Draw an arrow to the word (that it modifies)

13. Hugh Briss, who was a proud fellow, fell tragically.
14. Charlotte is the Queen City that truckers talk about.
15. Superman, to whom modern telephone booths present a problem, switched to revolving doors.

Adverb clause: Draw an arrow to the word that it modifies.

16. Josiah conveniently found *Deuteronomy* after Hilkiah hid it.
17. Our soldiers fought that others might live.
18. Because he wouldn't stand for it, he sat down.

(a) Enclose each (dependent clause) in parentheses.
   (Only the most common types of usage of clauses are given here.)
(b) Tell the grammatical usage of each clause.

1. That the tooth fairy didn't touch her pillow upset her.

2. The ball out of the park meant that the team danced elsewhere.

3. Did Buddy holler that he could play the guitar?

4. Lassie went to whoever fed him.

5. Jephthah was a warrior who did not put first things first.

6. Because you come to me, I have nought but love for you.

7. That she had close encounters of the fourth kind annoyed her.

8. "Top 40" for most means that one is turning forty-one.

9. The teacher stated that he was overworked, underpaid, and jaded.

10. The Godmother will grant three wishes to whoever sights the first twinkle.

11. Dentists have office music that spins a soporific spell.

12. The tick went crazy when he became the tock of the town.

13. That we still want to write sentences for this book is amazing.

14. Antinomianism means that one has special grace.

15. Tom swiftly stated that he could run fast.

16. For whatever reason he has, I cannot excuse him.

17. The rogue who painted well was hanged in a gallery.

18. If you accentuate the positive, you will eliminate the negative.

19. The mug that was from Germany was shot.

20. Darth turned vaguer as the stars warred on.

(a) Enclose each (dependent clause) in parentheses.
(b) Tell whether the clause is an adjective, an adverb, or a noun.
(c) Tell the grammatical usage of each clause.

1. Tell whether the clause is an adjective, an adverb, or a noun.

2. He is the Joe Smith who voted for Proposition XIV.

3. Because the tour book only included the Mideastern States, Doofo refused to enter Virginia from the south.

4. It is very apparent that waxing a car in sunlight is taxing.

5. The Sartoris that died in 1920 was Bayard III.

6. The little boy was not so independent as he thought; he still needed his mother at times.

7. The thought that his home was an igloo chilled the Eskimo.

8. The Banana Splits' antics, which were ludicrous at times, were not very palatable to me.

9. Guardhouses whirl like dervishes whenever they are caught in tornadoes.

10. Writing books for whoever will read them is a pleasure.

11. He has gone to a place where we all desire to go.

12. The prince's royalty seems to be a financial program, as he was just invested.

13. A person's home seems whatever he is.

14. Ours is a nation dedicated to God, in Whom we put our trust.

15. Sydney Carton was so brave that he gave his life for another.

(a) Enclose each (dependent clause) in parentheses.
(b) Tell whether the clause is an adjective, an adverb, or a noun.
(c) Tell the grammatical usage of each clause.

1. Would you give whichever Fuller he is the brush?

2. The Indians surrounded us, since we had intruded on their land.

3. At a time when all men should come to the aid of their country, no one should shirk his task.

4. My son, you should always assume the full responsibility which is yours to assume.

5. Although he could hear the wind gently soughing through the trees, his mind remained a maelstrom of despair.

6. No one can ever know what this book has meant to me.

7. "When am I going over to Scott's?" Edward asked.

8. However noisy her house remains, the student can always find refuge in her school library.

9. Is he the man whose head was laughed off?

10. That John belonged to the organization was attested to by his wearing purple amulets to work.

11. A person is only as good as he thinks he is.

12. My dog is bigger than your dog is.

13. For that member of the I.R.A. who is wearing both orange and green we award a brotherhood medal.

14. Observing that the human race is full of foibles, the philosopher smiled wryly.

15. He went swimming where the water was green.

(a) Enclose each (dependent clause) in parentheses.
(b) Tell whether the clause is an adjective, an adverb, or a noun.
(c) Tell the grammatical usage of each clause.

Note: Each sentence contains two (2) clauses.

1. The boys who train at "Muscle Beach" have larger biceps than most people.

2. As our flying saucer spun brightly into the western sky, we waved to the earthpeople on the field where we landed.

3. If the rain in Spain falls mainly on the plain, it is unlikely that the Pyrenees will suffer much from erosion.

4. The man who saved his money for years to return to the old country lost his small fortune the day before he was supposed to leave.

5. The Christmas tree that had been so beautiful was what the children remembered in the bleak January weather.

6. The guru from Nepal said that we are what we eat.

7. The fact that Mr. Eliot, who is known as a serious metaphysical poet, wrote "Old Possum's Book of Practical Cats" endears him to most middle-aged pedants.

8. Whoever has had a good friend will understand what it is to have lost one.

9. Give whomever you wish your class ring, but don't say that you weren't warned.

10. After all is said and done, the person who understands dependent clauses knows a great deal of grammar.

Write sentences which contain the following:

1. A noun clause used as the subject.

2. A noun clause used as the direct object.

3. A noun clause used as an appositive.

4. A noun clause used as a subjective complement.

5. An adjective clause used restrictively.

6. An adjective clause used non-restrictively.

7. An adjective clause with the relative pronoun omitted.

8. An introductory adverbial clause.

9. A terminal adverbial clause.

10. An elliptical adverbial clause.

1. Name the types of dependent clauses.

    _____   _____   _____

2. What is the difference between a dependent clause and an independent clause?

3. In regard to its usage, what is the difference between the connector of a noun clause and the connector of an adjective clause?

4. What is a subordinate conjunction?

5. What is a relative pronoun?

6. Where is an adjective clause placed in relation to the noun or pronoun that the clause modifies?

7. In regard to its punctuation, what is the difference between a restrictive clause and a non-restrictive clause?

8. Use the word *that* to introduce a noun clause.

9. Use the word *that* to introduce an adjective clause.

10. Use the word *that* to introduce an adverb clause.

PHRASES
PHRASES
PHRASES
PHRASES
PHRASES
PHRASES
PHRASES
PHRASES
PHRASES
PHRASES
PHRASES
PHRASES
PHRASES
PHRASES
PHRASES
PHRASES
PHRASES
PHRASES
PHRASES

1. What is a preposition?

2. What is a prepositional phrase?

3. List fifteen single words that could be used as prepositions.

    _____   _____   _____

    _____   _____   _____

    _____   _____   _____

    _____   _____   _____

    _____   _____   _____

4. List three pairs of words that could be used as prepositions.

    _____   _____   _____

5. Can three words be used as a single preposition?

6. May a prepositional phrase be used as an adverbial modifier or as an adjective modifier?

Enclose each (prepositional phrase) in parentheses.
Draw an arrow to the word the prepositional phrase modifies.

1.   The man (in the moon) was an astronaut.

2.   A house of cards will usually collapse.

3.   The grimy chap under the car was the mechanic.

4.   "The Man from U.N.C.L.E." is Napoleon Solo.

5.   The stories about Daniel Boone are largely true.

* * * * *

6.   The teacher sent the list (for summer reading).

7.   Renoir painted the women with beautiful complexions.

8.   Please eat the food before you.

9.   The storm ruined the farm beyond our land.

10.   I enjoy desserts like strawberry shortcake.

* * * * *

11.   The wind whistled (through the haunted house).

12.   The little Lotus hummed by the grandstand.

13.   Williams hit the ball over the fence.

14.   Sam Huff played despite injuries.

15.   The miler ran four laps around the track.

* * * * *

16.   (After the ball) Cinderella hurried home.

17.   Into the pool plunged the Olympic diver.

18.   Down the sidewalk he slithered.

19.   Onto the table sprang the cat.

20.   Between the trees we saw the Black Forest.

Enclose each (prepositional phrase) in parentheses.
Draw an arrow to the word the prepositional phrase modifies.

1. Time since that day has dragged for me.

2. Coops off the ground are preferred by chickens.

3. Mermaids underneath the boat could be seen around us.

4. The car upon the curb is certainly within the parking lines.

5. The noise throughout the house apparently came from the attic.

* * * * *

6. Toward the dawn a rosy glow of light spread over the sky in all directions.

7. Beyond the border, sounds of a revolution could be heard in the distance.

8. The pieces of rhubarb pie were divided equally among all of the members of the cooking class.

9. Between the twins I can't tell Howard at all.

10. Out of the past come the hoofbeats of the great horse Silver.

* * * * *

11. We returned to the house after the game.

12. Put the book on the table.

13. We play volleyball in the fall and basketball in the winter.

14. The cow jumped over the moon.

15. Little Willie fell into the cistern.

* * * * *

16. *Animals in Danger* is a book about animals in danger of extinction.

17. He likes frozen ice with syrup on it.

18. Put the new sentences under the phrase section.

19. The train went into the mountain and came out in pieces.

20. The snake sloughed his skin into the slough.

21. The boys on my team were excited.

22. The man in the helicopter signaled to the men in the raft.

23. The secretary in the office asked the man in the gray flannel suit for his name.

24. The giant man on the after-deck dug his fingers into Huck's shoulder and threw him off the deck and into the water.

25. Go into the hills and drive the Philistines out.

* * * * *

26. No one has seen the animal since Tuesday.

27. Bring your ticket to me, and I will save you a seat on the carousel.

28. Boys with special problems in English will be sent to the torture chamber.

29. Into the valley of death rode the six hundred.

30. He leadeth me beside the still waters.

* * * * *

31. Beside himself with grief he sat beside his mother.

32. The bandersnatch came burbling through the tulgey wood.

33. At market, at market they bought a fat pig.

34. In England, the king is never off the throne.

35. Over the river and through the woods to Grandmother's house we go.

* * * * *

36. Like her mother, she liked her father.

37. He was pushed into the revolving door and came out swinging.

38. Clarence was drowned in a butt of sack.

39. In spite of the danger, according to spectators, the fireman ran into the burning building and saved the fair damsel from smoke inhalation.

40. Night after night at the movies can be devastating.

1.   What are the three kinds of verbals?

_____   _____   _____

2   How do verbals differ from verbs?

3.   How are verbals like verbs?

4.   What is a gerund?

5.   Can a gerund have objects and modifiers?

6.   What is a gerund phrase?

7.   List the four forms of the gerund.

	Active	Passive
Present	_____	_____
Present Perfect	_____	_____

8.   How many ways may gerunds or gerund phrases be used in sentences?

9.   Are there any particular rules of punctuation for the gerund phrase?

10.   When a noun or a pronoun precedes a gerund, should it be made possessive?

Enclose each (gerund or gerund phrase) in parentheses.

. . . as subject

1. (Exercising) is good for the figure.

2. Praying is good for the soul.

3. Mowing will keep the grass trim.

4. Reading has many benefits.

5. Writing makes a person exact.

* * * * *

6. (Quitting jobs) can become habitual.

7. Lighting fires is the preoccupation of a pyromaniac.

8. Lighting lights is the highlight of the lamplighter's life.

9. Bugging parents seems to be some teenagers' reason for existence.

10. Girding loins is a prerequisite for battle.

* * * * *

11. (Swimming in the winter) is all right for polar bears.

12. Drinking on the house can be conducive to acrophobia.

13. Flying from the coop is tricky business, especially for chickens.

14. Listening to Crystal Canyon was a real treat.

15. Rising to the occasion sometimes requires real courage.

* * * * *

16. (Bending the knee to the floor) may result in knighthood or marriage.

17. Singing ballads in a barroom might lead to a contract with Folkways Records.

18. Riding horses for a hobby can be debilitating.

19. Tasting honey in the wrong places is fraught with peril.

20. Chasing the Joker in his Batcar was Batman's chief thrill.

. . .as direct object

21. Justice Douglas loves (hiking).

22. An active man can't stand sitting.

23. Kimball doesn't really like running.

24. The boy quit working.

25. He stopped thinking.

* * * * *

26. MacDonald dislikes (having farm animals).

27. Tarzan likes swinging from the trees.

28. He enjoyed growing a beard.

29. Camilla began doing "The Watusi."

30. The obsequious footman finally stopped holding the door open.

* * * * *

31. The Indian continued (standing in the rain forest in his hip boots).

32. The little boy disliked having nightmares about the ogre.

33. Frustrated poets stop writing poems.

34. The impresario wanted dancing all over the stage.

35. The insomniac tried sleeping in the daytime.

* * * * *

36. The President resented (seeing his caricature in *MAD* magazine).

37. The Allies began attacking the trenches at dawn.

38. Holmes enjoyed spying in the dark corners of Gothic chateaux.

39. The ground crew kept sweeping the sky with the searchlight.

40. Charon continued putting coins on the dead men's eyes.

. . . as subjective complement (predicate noun)

41. Mr. Churchill's avocation was (painting).

42. Pavlova's main interest was dancing.

43. A politician's goal will always be winning.

44. Seeing is believing.

45. Believing is seeing.

* * * * *

46. Lou Groza's strong point was (kicking field goals).

47. A favorite pastime of teenagers is talking on the telephone.

48. Jay's special aptitude is making speeches before large audiences.

49. One's goal should be searching for what always lies ahead.

50. The dishonest tailor's main fault was lining his own pockets.

* * * * *

. . . as object of the preposition

51. We left after (seeing the movie).

52. After seeing the movie, we left.

53. Before exercising, we jogged four laps.

54. We jogged four laps before exercising.

55. The class was exhausted from thinking and studying all day.

* * * * *

56. Before (shooting the foul shot) the player nervously bounced the ball on the floor.

57. After having won all of the marbles, the tow-headed kid gathered his wealth and hurried home.

58. The citizens had many different views on being called for jury duty.

59. The underprivileged person seems to be a new man since having been given a fresh start in life.

60. The new teacher had some radical ideas on the grading and correcting of compositions.

. . . as indirect object

61. He gave (going) a lot of consideration.
62. Joe gave weightlifting credit for his physique.

. . . as objective complement

63. I call that (good playing).
64. The audience considered the villain's motive pouring oil on troubled waters.

. . . as appositive

65. Nehru's task, (making peace), sometimes caused trouble.
66. The general's idea, attacking immediately, was poor strategy.
67. George enjoyed many happy hours at his favorite pastime, surfing.
68. The assignment, writing a short story, seemed impossible at first.
69. His job, approaching customers all day long, soon wore him out.

. . . as adverbial noun

70. He went (swimming).
71. He surfaced gasping.
72. The new neighbor came visiting.
73. Lady Brett Ashley went dancing all night long.
74. She went walking with the handsome stranger along the beach.

. . . with the possessive preceding

75. Nothing became him like (his going).
76. John's whining rose to a querulous pitch.
77. Does your mother know about my winning?
78. Edward's swimming the Channel was miraculous.
79. No one could foresee George's acquiring the bicycle so soon.

Enclose each (gerund or gerund phrase) in parentheses.
Tell the grammatical usage of each gerund.

1. Reading is enjoyable for most people.

2. Being shadowed can be very tiresome.

3. Writing compositions proved highly beneficial to the students.

4. Loafing at the local drugstore sometimes seems a waste of time.

5. Real athletes don't mind training or practicing.

* * * * *

6. The artist held his first showing in the old Studio Gallery.

7. Most Florentines disliked dining with the Borgias.

8. The riverboat gang resented losing money to Gaylord Mitty.

9. Doofo's favorite diversion is sailing frisbees from the study hall roof.

10. His ultimate downfall was not studying gerunds.

* * * * *

11. The boy's dream of glory was rescuing the head cheerleader from the path of an express train.

12. Kowalski's record was hitting seventy home runs in a season.

13. He disappeared after spending all of my allowance.

14. We took our shoes off upon entering the class on Far Eastern affairs.

15. In studying for the final exams, the ambitious students burned the midnight oil.

* * * * *

16. The editors of *The Evening Sun* take a dim view of our reading *The Morning News*.

17. His new business, raising cobras for fun and profit, proved hazardous.

18. We admired his obvious skill, threading a needle with his eyes shut.

19. Having asked the lovely lady to type our sentences was obviously a good move.

20. We eventually enjoyed going to summer school.

21. Playing "Taps" at Arlington had been Prewitt's chief military duty.

22. The best part of the party was the leaving of it.

23. Mothers can't stand the crying of children.

24. In proofreading, a person can make many mistakes.

25. George Fox enjoys three things — eating, watching television, and eating again.

* * * * *

26. The orchestra started playing a work by Shostakovitch.

27. Her chief dislike about the care of the automobile is washing it once a week.

28. His occupation, clipping coupons, has long fascinated me.

29. Near its source, the Seine delights in meandering through the village of Billy.

30. His filming of *The Seven Samurai* was, in my opinion, Kurosawa's greatest achievement as a film director.

* * * * *

31. Arguing unsuccessfully cannot possibly be one of Raymond Burr's failings as an actor.

32. The young prince's role was feigning poverty and assuming the guise of a pauper.

33. The Colonel's Lady could not stand being compared to Rosie O'Grady.

34. The diplomats, in not talking earnestly to each other, nearly caused a major war.

35. His pleasure, listening to the music of The Beatles at full volume, caused quite a stirring among his neighbors at 3:00 a.m.

* * * * *

36. Lady Macbeth mounted her broomstick and went soaring into the night.

37. The applicant who detested filling out the forms collapsed in a state of nervousness.

38. Subscribing to *The Boca Raton News* was the first step in moving to that distant tropical area.

39. Overcome with glee, the fiendish scientist rubbed her hands together in anticipating the outcome of her wild scheme.

40. The two brothers liked engaging each other in many types of athletic contests.

41. Socrates' main interests in life were debating and teaching.

42. Xantippe's main interest in life was thwarting Socrates.

43. The cellist gave playing for the President credit for his great success.

44. Maria Callas gave singing as the reason for her great breath control.

45. Fishing is fun — for everyone but the fish.

* * * * *

46. Rainsford disliked being hunted by the insane General Zaroff.

47. After having lost their twelfth straight game, the Erstwhiles sat glumly in their locker room.

48. His hobby was collecting girls.

49. Baiting a hook with worms can cause the squeamish to squeam.

50. Being seen in the Casbah with Pepe Le Moko proved to be a most unfortunate incident in the young diplomat's career.

* * * * *

51. Running for Congress on the Republican ticket can be futile in some states.

52. The roly-poly child enjoyed eating anything it could get its hands on.

53. Very few people can tolerate constant teasing.

54. Before pitching the ball, Gomez checked the runner at first.

55. The odd boy supported himself in college by doing odd jobs.

* * * * *

56. After having been reprimanded for smoking in the hall, the thoughtless student started chewing tobacco.

57. His job for the summer was lifting and carrying large bales of peat moss.

58. Sneezing for 2000 days straight is not a desirable record to set.

59. *Shoeing* a horse is different from *shooing* a horse.

60. Upon being voted the boy most likely not to succeed in college, Doofo began to study.

61. The students in the current events class enjoy the privilege of reading *Time* magazine in study hall.
62. Daydreaming was Walter Mitty's method of avoiding reality.
63. The three R's are reading, 'riting, and 'rithmetic.
64. The Burma Shave signs once had a classic jingle: "If one-arm driving is your sport, trade your car for a davenport."
65. Sometimes seeing is not believing.

* * * * *

66. The giant tom cat enjoyed sunning himself all day long and sleeping in Mr. Eliot's hat.
67. After seeing the hopelessness of the situation and realizing the futility of trying to do anything about the shortage of ammunition, the patrol withdrew from the area.
68. Participating in extra-curricular activities can be a very positive experience.
69. The prospect of having been seen in the beauty parlor as he was waiting for his mother haunted the young athlete.
70. Upon discovering that she had been accepted by Coliseum College, Melissa let her hair grow very long and began to wear leotards.

* * * * *

71. In most prep schools one usually begins the day by attending chapel service.
72. Although Bruce enjoyed watching television by the hour, he could upon occasion tear himself away for the purpose of eating and sleeping.
73. The young woman in the gray flannel power suit gave writing a try before she settled down and became a junior executive for a chain of toy stores.
74. One cannot help wondering what he will do after graduating from high school.
75. Studying gerunds can become a dull pastime.

* * * * *

76. Roosevelt's favorite diversion was collecting stamps.
77. By studying last week's game films, the members of the defensive backfield were able to see their mistakes clearly.
78. The whole class enjoyed reading *Huckleberry Finn*, but no one particularly liked *Innocents Abroad*.
79. Riding a motorcycle can be fun, but falling off can be painful.
80. After lecturing to the student body for over half an hour on safety precautions, the speaker tripped on the edge of the podium and fell into the front row seats.

81. Giving young children fountain pens can be disastrous.

82. The practice of contributing generously to worthy causes proves ennobling.

83. Martha gave practicing the piano a noble try, but she soon turned her attention to the neighborhood gang again.

84. The bane of Mary's existence is having to go to bed at 9:30 p.m. on school nights.

85. After arriving at sentence number eighty-five, the versatile young English teachers hated writing sentences with gerunds.

* * * * *

86. The idea of spending an entire month at the beach appealed to the boys.

87. Mr. Worthington's hobby, collecting rocks and minerals of the Piedmont area and classifying them, proved rewarding in the end.

88. Her work's being published at such an early age altered the writer's sense of values.

89. After having been smitten by the young lady's charms, Pendergrast grew very pale and wan.

90. The signing of the Declaration of Independence was one of the single most decisive acts in Western Civilization.

* * * * *

91. After having studied *Hamlet* for a week, the entire class was near paranoia.

92. The uncooperative boy resented being sent home from school.

93. Savoring the delicious aromas and seeing the buffet tables piled high with food was really more than the hungry athletes could stand.

94. Roark's occupation, working in a granite quarry, added to his overall knowledge of materials used in building.

95. The maroon team resented our rolling up such a high score.

* * * * *

96. The difference between listening to a recording and attending a concert astounds most people.

97. The many incidents of pilfering and plundering that followed in the wake of the tornado didn't say much for human behavior.

98. After hearing Mr. Auden on the subject of writing poetry, one would have to believe that the greatest obstacle for a young poet to overcome is taking himself too seriously.

99. Most children's greatest security measure is thumb-sucking; most adults' is viewing the "idiot box".

100. After shaping the entire course of modern art, Cézanne died thinking that he was a failure.

1. What are the three kinds of verbals?

   _____   _____   _____

2. How do verbals differ from verbs?

3. How are verbals like verbs?

4. What is a participle?

5. Can a participle have objects and modifiers?

6. What is a participial phrase?

7. List the five forms of the participle.

	Active	Passive
Present	_____	_____
Past	_____	
Present Perfect	_____	_____

8. What is the one participial form that differs from the gerund forms?

9. Are introductory participles or introductory participial phrases *always* set off by commas?

10. Do introductory participles or introductory participial phrases *always* modify the subject?

11. Are non-essential participles or participial phrases set off by commas?

Enclose each (participle or participial phrase) in parentheses.
Draw an arrow to the word the participle modifies.

. . . introductory participles

1. (Growling) the tiger seemed ferocious.
2. Having fallen, Humpty Dumpty lay in a thousand pieces.
3. Being seen, the sniper dropped her telescopic rifle and surrendered.
4. Hung, the pictures looked ludicrous.
5. Having been beaten, the Saxons still refused to capitulate.

* * * * *

. . . introductory participial phrases

6. (Beginning anew), each day seemed better than the last.
7. Bursting with pride, the mothers watched their children in the pageant.
8. Riding into the fading sunset, the man on the white horse threw away his silver bullets.
9. Appearing over the horizon, the *Santa Maria* frightened the Indians.
10. Growing into a beautiful swan, the ugly duckling was accepted by his peers.

* * * * *

. . . participle before word modified

11. The (whistling) kettle got on my nerves.
12. The rising sun appeared on time, as usual.
13. We heard the exciting news.
14. The crowd applauded the winning team.
15. The wounded hero smiled at the sniffling heroine.

* * * * *

. . . participle as subjective complement

16. The speaker was (boring).
17. A ride with a student driver can be exciting.
18. That girl is scintillating.
19. The octogenarian seemed tired.
20. We became concerned about the couple.

. . . participial phrase after word modified

21. The boy (playing the guitar) is good.
22. The girl appearing in the play is a friend of mine.
23. The packages being shipped overseas are duty-free.
24. Most of us loved the building being destroyed.
25. The troops looked as if they enjoyed the show given last night.

* * * * *

. . . non-restrictive participial phrase

26. Miss Universe, (appearing on television for the first time), mimicked Miss World's interesting walk.
27. J. Paul Getty's Rolls Royce, "Silver Cloud," being transported this week from England, is made of solid silver.
28. Old Sam, nonchalantly sitting overhead, was amused by the tigers beneath the eucalyptus tree.
29. Miss Monroe, seen in any critical light, was a wonderful comedienne.
30. *On the Road*, written by Jack Kerouac, gives an excellent picture of beatnik beneficence.

Enclose each (participle or participial phrase) in parentheses.
Draw an arrow to the word the participle modifies.

1. The running water splashed noisily.

2. The sinking ship went down quickly.

3. All of us saw the wrecked airplane.

4. Many of the elves repaired the broken toys.

5. The drowning man grabbed the floating buoy.

* * * * *

6. Falling, the balloon burst in the tree.

7. Laughing, the audience forgot the oppressive heat.

8. Having won, the golfer headed for the showers.

9. Having been apprehended, the reckless driver lost his license.

10. Having resisted and endured, the members of the underground rejoiced on V-E Day.

* * * * *

11. Missing the target completely, Little John blushed with shame.

12. Having seen the last of Josiah Crabtree, the Rover Boys relaxed for a while.

13. Being seen in the tavern, Mr. Beauchamp hastened home.

14. Reviewed for the first time, Carmen seemed to be a flop.

15. Having been shot twice, the man-eater headed for the bush.

* * * * *

16. The boy doing the puzzle is a friend of mine.

17. The girl wearing the sack dress is the president of the class.

18. The campers, having finished their meal, put out the fire.

19. The empire of the Mayans, having reached a peak of development, began a long decline.

20. Miss Minerva, disgusted and despairing, called loud and long for William Green Hill.

21. We noticed the dripping water.

22. Father mended the broken doll.

23. Walking rapidly in the sun, the safari began to tire.

24. Having enjoyed the circus, the family returned home.

25. Sensing the danger in advance, Starbuck would not lower the boat after dark.

* * * * *

26. Having sensed that the intruder was a S.M.E.R.S.H. agent, Miss Moneypenny called Mr. Bond.

27. Waiting to hear the results of the fifth race, the bookies gathered around the wire.

28. The Shakespearean dressing room was known as the tiring house.

29. The bound edition of *Wuthering Heights* has disappeared from the library.

30. Singing happily, the milkmaid completed her chores.

* * * * *

31. Burned to a frazzle, the turkey looked like a giant cinder.

32. The spent athlete collapsed at the finish line.

33. The mutilated coin bore a resemblance to today's quarter.

34. A drawn-and-quartered person is uncomfortable, to say the least.

35. His hair was raised by the shocking tale of horror.

* * * * *

36. Henry's hair, bleached the color of the sun, was very brittle at the ends.

37. The pigs returning from the trough had indeed enjoyed their repast.

38. Broken milk bottles on cold mornings can be very disheartening.

39. People in hot weather subconsciously enjoy the whirring sounds of electric fans.

40. The bare bear bore his indignity with feigned indifference.

41. The baby looked at the broken toy and babbled.

42. Many valuable teaching tools exist today.

43. There were many tired soldiers on the beaches at Dunkirk.

44. The beating rain hammered upon the tin roof.

45. A revised edition of *Ivanhoe* has been published.

* * * * *

46. Having run into the kitchen, Misty saved herself from the storm.

47. Carrying with them the use of iron weapons, the Hittites invaded Anatolia about 1100 B.C.

48. Falling gracefully, the leaf landed on the window-sill.

49. Having taught arithmetic for fifty years, the teacher retired.

50. Having presented *Murder in the Cathedral* for the first time, the entire cast was absent from school the next day.

* * * * *

51. The actor making the horrible face won the part of Frankenstein's monster.

52. Napoleon, having been defeated at Waterloo, was soon thereafter exiled.

53. The architect showing us the house has won many prizes for his designs.

54. The aging seamstress made a costume consisting of rags.

55. Our boat, tied to its moorings last night, has drifted away.

* * * * *

56. Having slipped past the guards, the escaped prisoners sighed with relief.

57. Dante, conducted through the regions of the inferno, learned a great deal about the degraded human condition.

58. Finishing their novel, the team of aspiring writers relaxed for the first time in many months.

59. The wind, whistling through the ancient, crumbling walls, frightened the searching boys.

60. Stripped of his rank, the disgraced soldier was drummed out of the corps, defeated in person and broken in spirit.

61. Seeing the calliope, the child became excited.

62. Perking up its ears, the little chipmunk darted into the rocks.

63. Seen for the first time, *Gone With the Wind* is panoramic in its conception and scope.

64. Shot from a cannon day after day, Zachini became gun shy and very deaf.

65. Hearing the noise and smelling the smoke, Mr. Polly ran into the street.

* * * * *

66. The aging night watchman, carrying his torch and nightstick, trudged wearily along the corridor.

67. The sprinter running in the second lane won by a full stride.

68. The nations admitted to the United Nations recently add to the growing confusion on the East River.

69. The President, stricken with a severe case of flu, caused confusion on Wall Street.

70. Many men, feeling very young and energetic, tend to exhaust themselves through over-exertion.

* * * * *

71. Feeling faint, the choir member sat down during the Doxology.

72. Learning that Lois Lane was in grave danger, Our Hero, Superman, shot through the air with the speed of a bullet.

73. Having been elected president of her class for the last three years, Strongfort took the balloting in stride.

74. The play being read by the sophomores is an adaptation of *Billy Budd*.

75. Peter Lorre, seen in any situation in any movie, is a sinister, slightly suspicious character.

* * * * *

76. Having learned only recently that girls are different from boys, Doofo took a new interest in life.

77. The pigs, squealing and running in every direction, caused a tremendous uproar in the barnyard.

78. Laps run for punishment are unpleasant at best.

79. Huck Finn, having witnessed mankind's evils and injustices, took a dim view of the human condition.

80. The new building given by the alumni will be used as a fine arts center.

81. Having awakened the entire student body with his flugelhorn, Doofo was severely chastened by the prefects.
82. The football used in today's game will be kept permanently in the trophy case.
83. Who is the girl playing goalie?
84. A rose called by any other name smells just as sweet.
85. Stymied by the adroit moves of the older woman, the young chess genius haltingly advanced her bishop.

* * * * *

86. Mr. Kennedy, known for his charm and urbane humor, made a great impression on the youth of this country.
87. Every morning the turncoat was awakened by a rooster crowing outside his cell.
88. Discipline, seen as an end in itself, is most effective if it is voluntary.
89. The person being ridden through the streets of Paris in a crude tumbril is none other than Mr. Defarge.
90. Writing, having written, being written, written, and having been written, the participles dangled grotesquely.

* * * * *

91. Fearing that the end of the world was at hand, the members of the small religious sect gathered together for incantations.
92. The movie currently playing at the Bijou has a sign saying, "Standing Room Only."
93. Mr. Mephistopheles, having finally accepted the fact that he was wrong, terminated the debate, turned on his heel, and stalked out of the room.
94. Playing Drop the Handkerchief and laughing in childish glee, the kindergarten class did not see the gigantic dragon behind the japonica tree.
95. The cowboy being carried through the streets of Laredo in the pine box was a little too slow on the draw.

* * * * *

96. Becoming aware of the growing animosity toward the foreigners, the State Department tried to put a stop to the mounting xenophobia.
97. Captain Queeg, having sighted the shellbursts while still far from the landing beach, dropped some yellow dye markers and ordered the *Caine* to put about.
98. Being viewed at the National Gallery for the first time in America, the Mona Lisa drew enormous crowds of art lovers, tourists, and curiosity seekers.
99. The participles studied in class illustrated all possible uses of these verbal adjectives.
100. Having been publicly stripped of his academic standing, the erstwhile teacher stood humbly by as the administrator read off the charges against him and, in a dramatic gesture, broke his red pencil.

1. What are the three kinds of verbals?

    _____   _____   _____

2. How do verbals differ from verbs?

3. How are verbals like verbs?

4. What is an infinitive?

5. Can an infinitive have objects and modifiers?

6. What is an infinitive phrase?

7. List the four forms of the infinitive.

<table>
<tr><td></td><td>Active</td><td>Passive</td></tr>
<tr><td>Present</td><td>_____</td><td>_____</td></tr>
<tr><td>Present Perfect</td><td>_____</td><td>_____</td></tr>
</table>

8. May the sign of an infinitive (to) be omitted in a sentence?

9. Are there any particular rules of punctuation for the infinitive?

Enclose each (infinitive or infinitive phrase) in parentheses.

. . . as subject

1. (To err) is human.

2. To love should be the goal of mankind.

3. To hate is soul-consuming.

4. To walk was the jockey's way of relaxation.

5. To exist requires courage.

* * * * *

6. (To be in ignorance of the law) is no excuse.

7. To sleep soundly through the ringing of the alarm is perfect bliss.

8. To have loved and lost is better than not having loved at all.

9. To ride in a jeep for seven days would make one weak.

10. To wash dishes is the bane of many a housewife's existence.

. . . as direct object

11. Ryun wanted (to win)

12. Phineas wished to travel.

13. Saint-Exupery liked to fly.

14. The child learned to swim.

15. Harriet loves to cook.

* * * * *

16. Many children like (to buy frilly things).

17. Children love to ride spotted horses bareback in the sun.

18. Johnny refuses to surf in his new wetsuit.

19. The bells ceased to toll in the little village.

20. He wanted to hear that song again.

. . . as subjective complement (predicate noun)

21. His ambition was (to succeed).

22. Wilma's goal was to win.

23. Our main purpose had been to see.

24. Axel's aim was to heist.

25. The President's mission had been to mediate.

* * * * *

26. Happiness is (to learn that there will be no school because of snow).

27. Happiness is to study infinitives.

28. Happiness is to know your College Board scores are good.

29. His one desire is to beat the White Knight to the dirty clothes.

30. My wish is to sell the '28 Rolls for $2400.

. . . as appositive

31. The Riddler's secret desire, (to sing), was finally realized.

32. His ambition, to cogitate, was soon thwarted by the small children.

33. Charles Horse's purpose, to hurt, soon became a reality.

34. The runner's goal, to break the existing record, should be realized this Saturday.

35. Dr. Schweitzer's lifelong plan, to teach and to heal, was very noble.

* * * * *

36. Kit accomplished his plan, (to draw well for his parents).

37. The speaker's intention, to inspire his audience, failed from the start.

38. His desire, to succeed in his chosen vocation, led him to great heights.

39. Madame Curie's ambition, to gain recognition in the field of medicine, was fulfilled.

40. Icarus' goal, to fly first, ended with his wings melting.

. . . as an adjective

41. The apartment (to let) was a hovel.
42. A good book to read is *Lady Loverly's Chatter*.
43. Now is a good time to master the subject of verbals.

. . . as an adverb

44. My friend came (to see me).
45. We exercise to keep healthy.
46. The visiting team came to play.

. . with the sign (to) missing

47. Let (us pray).
48. Let me go with you.
49. To relax and play are important.
50. The dreamy boy wanted to sculpt and paint.

. . . as subject, with the expletive (it)

51. It is nice (to know you).
52. It is easy to understand infinitives.
53. It is silly not to study.

. . . as object of a preposition

54. He was about (to go).
55. She had no desire except to stay.

. . . as object of verbal

56. Wanting (to win too much), he became blind to good sportsmanship.
57. Wanting to win too much can lead to poor sportsmanship.

. . . in an infinitive clause

58. The country wanted (the folk groups to play better music).
59. The team wished John to be captain.

THE INFINITIVE AND THE INFINITIVE PHRASE

Enclose each (infinitive or infinitive phrase) in parentheses.
Tell the grammatical usage of each infinitive.

1. To study medicine was her only wish.

2. To learn English seemed unimportant.

3. The homesick camper wanted to go home.

4. The rowdy guest hated to leave the party.

5. The time to study is now.

* * * * *

6. The historic homes to visit were pointed out to us.

7. We go to school to learn how to function as human beings.

8. The team worked hard to score.

9. To decide is the mark of a mature person.

10. Holden Caulfield wanted to quit school and work in a filling station out West.

* * * * *

11. To see, the blind man had an operation.

12. A very good book to read is *Raintree County*.

13. The hoods wanted to go to work by the way of the poolroom.

14. To move quickly and quietly was the cat burglar's desire.

15. To cross the desert, the camel loaded up on water.

* * * * *

16. To forgive is divine.

17. I have no time to spare for trivial things.

18. The attempt to kick the field goal failed.

19. The students were anxious to please the teacher.

20. He wanted to see the movie *Stalag 17* again.

21. The right thing to do isn't always easy.

22. The place to find the pot of gold is just over the horizon.

23. The final will be the hardest examination to take.

24. This work was to have been completed by now.

25. All seems to be in order.

* * * * *

26. Lewis waited to ask the Headmaster for his permission.

27. Many adventurers went to California to seek gold.

28. To be home early, the commuter took the 4:10.

29. To live in Tahiti, a person cannot sponge off the natives.

30. To pass the course, he will have to study.

* * * * *

31. It is a nuisance to save trading stamps.

32. To be a professional requires great skill.

33. To occasionally split an infinitive seems perfectly natural.

34. James Bond had to go to Haiti after Mr. Big.

35. The farmer tried to grow a type of hybrid corn suited to the climate.

* * * * *

36. He liked to shoot off fireworks.

37. The bounty hunter's job was to track down bounties.

38. Cleopatra wanted to protect Ptolemy.

39. The ambition of the stagehand was to act.

40. MacArthur's famous vow, to return to the Philippines, was fulfilled.

41. Hitler's mad plan was to conquer the world.

42. To play the role of Medea can prove quite challenging.

43. Arnold doesn't want to stop playing golf.

44. Leander had no alternative except to swim.

45. Try to start the exercise again.

* * * * *

46. To show sympathy for Jack, Jill fell down the hill.

47. To diet most effectively, a person should refrain from eating.

48. The night made the trees too dark to see.

49. He ran home to tell his mother the news of his narrow escape.

50. The suit was ready to be worn.

* * * * *

51. Nice is a nice town to visit.

52. The play we wanted to see just ended its season on Broadway.

53. The landlord hung out the "Apartment to Rent" sign.

54. The best suits to buy are made of Dacron and wool.

55. A good place to have lived would have been in Paris in the 1920's.

* * * * *

56. To be or not to be is the question.

57. The acid test is to try the crossword puzzle using a pen.

58. The undisciplined boy is learning to control himself.

59. No one should ever try to speak in class without thinking first.

60. She went to join in the search for the lost spelunker.

61. Our newspaper staff tried to publish a paper that was mature and at the same time humorous.

62. After the game we were convinced that the other team had really come to play ball.

63. The best thing to do in an emergency is to keep calm and collected.

64. To run and play freely was the haunting desire of most of the children in the ward.

65. Dawkins' alternate plan, to play professional football, was thwarted when he became a Rhodes Scholar.

* * * * *

66. Let us pray.

67. Apparently wanting to come in the house, Bowser tore a gigantic hole in the front screen.

68. The current fad among the girls at our school is to wear green lipstick and long white eyelashes.

69. Citation's owners expected to win the Triple Crown in racing.

70. It is too hot to breathe.

* * * * *

71. It is nice to know you.

72. Betty's plan was to go to the museum as often as she could.

73. The Romantic poets were too concerned with their imaginations to be overly conscious of their minds.

74. Beware of anyone who says he has a deal to work with you.

75. To live is to suffer.

* * * * *

76. Hurlburt enlisted in the Marines to serve for two years and then signed for another hitch to be with her buddies.

77. The circumstances were too complicated to explain to anyone.

78. After trying to climb the Matterhorn, the fellows in our group asked only to rest and sleep and be left alone for several days.

79. The books we were given to read in health class seemed to be written by the birds and the bees.

80. To live without fear, to be free to shape our own destinies, and to pursue happiness are fundamental to the American dream.

81. Not to study was the only alternative.

82. Matilda did not want to attend the waltz with Wallaby.

83. Mallory's plan was to ascend the east wall of the mountain.

84. Wanting to gather the ferny blue wildflowers, the botanist climbed further out on the dangerous precipice.

85. We came to see the man who has the home to sell.

* * * * *

86. Give me two hamburgers to go.

87. The prisoner of war was happy just to breathe fresh air again.

88. Let us see what work there is for us to do.

89. To find an infinitive in a sentence is easy.

90. To do the work seemed foolish, but it had to be done.

* * * * *

91. A wise thing to practice is self-control.

92. To watch television constantly should be a form of punishment.

93. When the Hebrew king went forth to conquer the Philistines, he had Yahweh on his side.

94. The sophomore boy was so attracted to the freshman girl that he intentionally tried to fail all of his subjects.

95. The ball player's main goal in life, to score the winning touchdown in the final seconds of the last game of the season in his senior year, seems to be rather impractical.

* * * * *

96. To fish, and swim, and loll around in the sun were the things that Huck and Jim really enjoyed.

97. The attractive girl told Doofo that it was nice to meet him, a situation which caused the boy to get very flustered.

98. The surgeon planned to tell the patient why she had to operate.

99. To enjoy the freedom one can experience in America is a divine blessing.

100. Let us leave the subject of infinitives and go on to greater things.

(a) **Enclose each (verbal phrase) in parentheses.**

Gerund as subject

1.   Finding frisky foxes frets Fran.

Gerund as direct object

2.   The bread needs kneading.

Gerund as subjective complement (predicate noun)

3.   His happiness on Mondays is watching M.A.S.H. re-runs.

Gerund as object of the preposition

4.   Integrity lies somewhat upon telling the truth.

Participles as adjectives

5.   Weak-kneed from fear, the burly linesman keeled over.

6.   Tickling the ivories, George played a merry tune.

7.   The elephant with the too tickled ivories trumpeted loudly.

8.   The tickled tick developed a nervous tic.

9.   Doc's forte was doing well in school.

10.   Anna became tired from the six basketball overtimes.

Infinitive as subject

11.   To become a tree is a seed's ambition.

Infinitive as direct object

12.   Harvey wanted to become visible only at 3' 4 1/2".

Infinitive as subjective complement (predicate noun)

13.   Mohammed's ambition was to bring a mountain to him.

Infinitive as adjective

14.   The book to buy now is *Junior Words, Phrases, Clauses.*

Infinitive as adverb

15.   To see your child's teacher, watch him play school.

(a) **Enclose each (verbal phrase) in parentheses.**
(b) **Tell the grammatical use of each phrase.**

Gerunds

1. Slaloming across the ocean is hard work.

2. George loved watching *Star Trek*.

3. Haisley's occupation was managing teams.

4. In the taking of money, he fell over the brink.

Participles

5. Playing the harpsichord, Stefan attracted a crowd.

6. Winning the humans over with fire, Prometheus did himself a disservice.

7. An intriguing symbiosis occurred between the angel and Jacob.

8. John Clark became a shining example of an Eagle Scout.

Infinitives

9. To dream the impossible dream caused him sleepless nights.

10. The sister wanted to acquire a better habit.

11. Freddie's wish was to make the Varsity Baseball Team.

12. To see a child's parent, watch him play house.

(a) Enclose each (verbal phrase) in parentheses.

(b) Tell whether the phrase is a gerund, a participle, or an infinitive.

(c) Tell the grammatical usage of each phrase.

1. In becoming Mrs. August, Lois was married in August.

2. Having had two lessons in karate, she became an expert in hand signals.

3. The Frido Bandido has to come to my office.

4. They heard him swearing a blue streak.

5. Caesar, crossing the Rubicon, had come, had seen, and had conquered.

6. Let us reason together.

7. Running the mile must be accomplished in less than four minutes.

8. The house, carried down the street on a flat-bed, was aflame.

9. One knows that it is nice to pick one's friends.

10. Her being elected governor astonished her supporters.

11. Hitch was quietly engaging.

12. To put one's best foot forward properly leaves little space for teeth.

13. His daily duty, placing the flag on the pole, never uplifted him.

14. Ripple on forever, you rapidly racing rivulet.

15. To do his best, the Boy Scout pledged.

    (a) Enclose each (verbal phrase) in parentheses.

    (b) Tell whether the phrase is a gerund, a participle, or an infinitive.

    (c) Tell the grammatical usage of each phrase.

1. "I am not about to go with you," she said haltingly.

2. Shedding along, the dog broadcast a mat of thick, white fur.

3. The Little Leaguer, piping lustily, casually fielded the line drive.

4. We called that poor judging.

5. The principal gave the wearing of shorts his every consideration.

6. The "Made in the Black Forest" label had been clearly visible to the elves.

7. His preoccupation was to work before his main job.

8. Come fly with me.

9. Are you going to graduate, Mrs. Robinson?

10. The Ambassador's task, to talk turkey to the Turks, earned him the reputation of loquaciousness.

11. The wrestler purposely faltered to purchase a better hold on his opponent.

12. Rodin seemed thinking about his sculpture.

13. Edward loved wheeling his bike with no hands.

14. Janice, patiently waiting for me, watched the completion of the first chapter.

15. George's joy was wearing his antlers of oak.

(a) Enclose each (verbal phrase) in parentheses.

(b) Tell whether the phrase is a gerund, a participle, or an infinitive.

(c) Tell the grammatical usage of each phrase.

Note: Each sentence contains two (2) verbal phrases.

1. Not to experience anxiety is not to be human.

2. Knocked down in every round, the quickly aging fighter hung on until the fight was over.

3. Drifting slowly to earth in a parachute is almost euphoric after the trauma of jumping from the airplane.

4. The previews of attractions coming next showed scenes from the first Ingmar Bergman film ever shown in America.

5. Having anticipated that he would fail English, Doofo tried very hard to impress his teacher.

6. The milers went out for cross country in the fall to build up their bodies and increase their endurance.

7. Waiting for the important phone call, the coed tried to do her homework.

8. It made us angry to find out that the book to read for parallel was not in the library.

9. His method of relaxing after a hard day's work was playing handball.

10. The use of verbals is one of the single most important developments in man's ability to communicate clearly, since they allow us to use any verb as another part of speech.

Write sentences which contain the following:

1. A gerund phrase used as a subject.

2. A gerund phrase used as the direct object.

3. A gerund phrase used as an appositive.

4. A gerund phrase used as a subjective complement.

5. A participial phrase used restrictively.

6. A participial phrase used non-restrictively.

7. An introductory participial phrase.

8. An infinitive phrase used as the subject.

9. An infinitive phrase used as an adjective.

10. An infinitive phrase used as an adverb.

1. Name the three types of verbals.

    _____   _____   _____

2. What is the difference between a verbal and a verb?

3. May a verbal have an object and modifiers, as a verb may?

4. Which two verbals may be used as nouns?

5. Which two verbals may be used as adjectives?

6. Which two verbals may be used as adverbs?

7. How are introductory participles punctuated?

8. How are introductory infinitives used as modifiers punctuated?

9. How are introductory prepositional phrases containing a gerund as the object usually punctuated?

10. How are non-restrictive verbals punctuated?

FINAL EXERCISE: THE CLASSICAL QUIZ

(a) Identify each *italicized* clause, phrase, or verbal as noun, adjective, or adverb. (2) means there are two items in the sentence.

(b) Tell the grammatical usage of each clause, phrase, or verbal.

1. *To resist him that is set in authority* is evil. (2)
   -Ptahhotep

2. *If a man destroy the eye of another man*, they shall destroy his eye.
   -Hammurabi

3. The man *who acts the least*, upbraids the most.
   -Homer

4. The lot of man; *to suffer* and *to die*. (2)
   -Homer

5. Tis a vain and impotent thing *to bewail the dead*.
   -Stesichorus

6. In *fleeing the ashes* he's fallen into the coals.
   -Alcaeus

7. I am sure *the grapes are sour*.
   -Aesop

8. "Honor thy father and thy mother" stands *written among the three laws* of *most revered righteousness*. (2)
   -Aeschylus

9. I benefit myself in *aiding him*.
   -Sophocles

10. I think *that Fortune watcheth o'er our lives, /Surer than we*. (2)
    -Euripides

11. The life *which is unexamined* is not worth living. (2)
    -Socrates

12. Brekeke-kesh, koash, koash.
    -Aristophanes
    (This one simply looked *intriguing*. We also could not parse it.)

13. The direction *in which education starts a man* will determine his future life.
    -Plato

14. Give me *where to stand*, and I will move the earth.
    -Archimedes

15. In fine, nothing is said now *that has not been said before*.
    -Terence

PROBLEMS
PROBLEMS
PROBLEMS
PROBLEMS
PROBLEMS
PROBLEMS
PROBLEMS
PROBLEMS
PROBLEMS
PROBLEMS
PROBLEMS
PROBLEMS
PROBLEMS
PROBLEMS
PROBLEMS
PROBLEMS
PROBLEMS

PROBLEMS

1. Does the use of a pronoun in a dependent clause determine the case of that pronoun?

   _____

2. Are the nominative forms of pronouns — *who* and *whoever* — used for subjects and subjective complements?

   _____

3. Are the objective forms of pronouns — *whom* and *whomever* — used for direct objects of prepositions?

   _____

4. Does the adjectival form *whose* always show possession? _____

5. Are non-restrictive (non-essential) adjective and adverb clauses always set off by commas?

   _____

6. Do non-restrictive (non-essential) adverb clauses at the end of sentences begin with *as*, *since*, and *for*, meaning *because*?

   _____

7. Since we don't set off a dependent adverb clause beginning with the word *because*, could we say that clause is restrictive?

   _____

8. Is Santa's wife ever restrictive of Mr. Claus' whereabouts? _____

9. Are introductory adverb clauses set off by commas? _____

10. Are introductory verbals and verbal phrases not used as subjects set off by commas?

    _____

The use of a pronoun in a dependent clause determines the case of that pronoun.

Nominative

(<u>who</u>: subject) She is a girl (<u>who</u> <u>studies</u>.)

(<u>who</u>: subject) This is Mollie, (<u>who</u> <u>studies</u> diligently.)

(<u>whoever</u>: subject) Give the award to (<u>whoever</u> <u>deserves</u> it.)

(<u>whoever</u>: subject) We will go with (<u>whoever</u> <u>offers</u> us a ride.)

(<u>who</u>: predicate nominative) We would like to know (<u>who</u> you <u>are</u>.)

Objective

(<u>whom</u>: direct object) She is a girl (whom <u>I</u> <u>know</u>.)

(<u>whom</u>: direct object) This is my wife, (whom <u>you</u> <u>have met</u>.)

(<u>whomever</u>: direct object) Give the award to (whomever <u>you</u> <u>choose.</u>)

(<u>whom</u>: object of the preposition) This is the person (to whom <u>you</u> <u>should refer.</u>)

Exercise: Write in the correct form — <u>who</u>, <u>whom</u>, or <u>whose</u> — in the blank spaces below.

1.   Beaufort is a fine young man _____ graduated in three years.

2.   That was Beaufort, _____ I just told you about.

3.   Do you lend your car to anyone _____ asks for it?

4.   Did you lend your car to someone _____ you don't know well?

5.   There is a girl in Who's Who _____ sits next to me in Latin class.

6.   An owl is a bird _____ whoooooooes all night long.

7.   Any owl _____ is in *Who's Who* is probably a fine hooter or someone _____ doesn't give a hoot.

8.   The Who is a well-known rock group _____ really rocks.

9.   The person _____ picture you admire is Sophia Loren.

10. Ms. Loren, of _____ we were just speaking, is one actress _____ doesn't put up any false fronts.

NON-ESSENTIAL (NON-RESTRICTIVE) ADJECTIVE AND ADVERB CLAUSES

Use commas to set off (1) non-restrictive adjective clause and (2) non-restrictive adverb clauses at the end of sentences (beginning with *as*, *since*, or *for*, meaning *because*).

restrictive adjective clause

Dr. Schweitzer was a man who cared.

non-restrictive adjective clause

This is a picture of Dr. Schweitzer, who devoted his life to helping others.

restrictive adverb clause

Alfred E. Newman smiled because he was happy. (Note that clauses at the end of sentences beginning with *because* are not set off.)

non-restrictive adverb clause

Alfred smiled, for he was happy.

non-restrictive adverb clause

Alfred smiled, since he was happy.

Exercise: Set off the non-restrictive clauses in the following sentence with commas.

1. That is a man who has prodigious strength.
2. That was Souperman who advertises soup.

3. The girl whom we just passed goes to our school.
4. Ophelia Orphal whom we just passed is homecoming queen.

5. Did you meet the novelist whose book we studied?
6. I met Kurt Vonnegut whose *Slaughterhouse Five* is one of my favorite novels.

7. The book that you're studying contains hundreds of thought-provoking sentences.
8. *Words, Phrases, Clauses* which you're using contains many characters but a rather weak plot.

9. Mallory climbed the Matterhorn because it was there.
10. The students climbed the water tower since they had nothing better to do.

11. The Beatles were popular because they looked like four Raggedy Andys.
12. The Monkeys were popular for they modeled their style on the Beatles'.

13. We used to read the *New Yorker* because it was there.
14. We now read *New York* as its new style is trendy and upbeat.

15. Soccer is very popular because people get their kicks from the game.
16. Doofo needed our solicitous succor for his friends mistook his head for a soccer ball.

Use commas to set off introductory adverb clauses.

(introductory adverb clause)

Because the tortoise beat the hare, nonjoggers should rejoice.

Exercise: Set off each introductory clause in the following sentences with a comma.

when	1.	When day is done shadows fall.
when	2.	When the play is done the curtain falls.
if	3.	If it snows we won't have school.
if	4.	If we're well-schooled we won't be snowed by advertising on television.
while	5.	While disorder reigns confusion blossoms.
while	6.	While the rains poured down the Japanese cherry blossoms blew in the wind.
although	7.	Although *Moby Dick* is a whale of a story there's something fishy about Ahab.
although	8.	Although whales eternally fight giant squid no one has written a novel about them.
after	9.	After we won the meet we celebrated by having steak for dinner.
after	10.	After we pulled up stakes we raced to meet the winning celebrity.
since	11.	Since Doofo was talking in line the teacher made him stand in the corner.
since	12.	Since Doofo had cornered the girls they weren't impressed by his obvious line.
even	13.	Even though it is raining cats and dogs are still fighting.
even	14.	Even though cats and dogs are still fighting there is seldom a reign of terror by either party.
as	15.	As Nero fiddled Rome burned.
as	16.	As Zero Mostel fiddled *Fiddler on the Roof* set Broadway on fire.
as if	17.	As if death weren't enough we still have taxes.
as if	18.	As if he were an auto-taxidermist Doofo stuffed himself with junk food.
because	19.	Because introductory adverb clauses are usually easy to we usually remember to set them off.
because	20.	Because of his spotty career in English class Doofo gave up on all punctuation.

INTRODUCTORY VERBALS

Use commas to set off introductory verbals and verbal phrases not used as subjects.

Do not set off with commas.

(subject/gerund) *Shopping* is fun.

(subject/gerund phrase) *Habituating hat shops* can become wearing.

(subject/infinitive phrase) *To forgive everyone for everything* is not too divine.

Set off with commas.

(participial phrase) Wearing a habit, the nun thanked Holden for his donation.

(prepositional phrase, with gerund object) By wearing out bad habits, we become stronger in character.

(infinitive phrase) To improve character, one should wear a tight-fitting hat occasionally.

Exercise: Set off introductory verbals and verbal phrases *not* used as subjects.

Participals

1. Smiling the teacher gave Doofo a zero.
2. Smiling his lethal smile Walter Mitty zeroed in on the Red Baron.

3. Being spotted the girls returned to school.
4. Being spotted in the Dirty Dawg Saloon the boys returned to school.

Infinitives

5. To excel you must never give up.
6. To excel in marathon running you must become a mystical stoic.

7. To be published your Great American Novel must be great.
8. To be published in a periodical your article must meet a pressing deadline.

Gerunds (used as objects of prepositions)

9. By watching we gained an insight into weighty problems
10. By watching weight watchers watch their weight we gained patience.

11. After having been sold the little puppy looked sad.
12. After having been sold by the *nouveau* poor school teacher to help defray the cost of real estate taxes the poor pitiful puppy posed as a playfully prostrate parcel of pooch on the projecting porch parapet.

Gerunds (used as subjects)

13. Punctuating introductory verbals is easy.
14. Having studied verbals improved our sentence structure.

15. Verbalizing too often might prove demoralizing.
16. Verbalizing can verbalize verbal verbiage verbally.

I. Choose the correct form of the pronoun in each sentence below.

1. Spiderman is a person (who, whom) spins quite a yarn.

2. Spiderman is a victim (who, whom) became trapped in his own web.

3. Spiderman is a nut (who, whom) we all feel sorry for.

4. We will present the *Mad* magazine award to (whoever, whomever) is totally disoriented.

5. We will present the *Mad* magazine award to (whoever, whomever) we believe is worthy of the honor.

II. Set off non-restrictive adjective and adverb clauses

1. *Gone With the Wind* which was written by Margaret Mitchell was made into one of the most successful movies of all time.

2. *Catcher in the Rye* is by J. D. Salinger who chronicles a young boy's search for values and meaning in an indifferent world.

3. Doofo began to study English for his grade average was plunging lower and lower.

4. The audience wept since the heroine was trampled to death by a small herd of turtles.

5. The literary magazine was called *Emanon* because the writers couldn't think of a title other than "no-name" spelled backwards.

III. Set off introductory adverb clauses.

1. After the play was over we had a cast party.

2. After we presented Rajah Bombast from Bombay we had a caste party.

3. If all men are created equal why are some seemingly created more equal than others?

4. Although explicit topic sentences are essential to most paragraphs they can sometimes be implied.

5. When you want to strengthen your paragraphs use reasons and concrete examples in your supporting sentences.

IV. Set off any verbals and verbal phrases not used as subjects of a sentence.

1. Running up Heartbreak Hill the runner dreamed of a nice cool drink and a hammock in the shade.

2. Being run to the point of exhaustion the players almost decided to boycott early field hockey practice.

3. To carry anything to its logical conclusion one must have some end in view.

4. After voting for Senator Babbitt Gatewater Claghorn we tried desperately to deny the fact.

5. To have flunked out of Podunk U the left-handed Doofo must have felt gauche-awful.

Correct any errors in the case of pronouns and any errors in punctuation in the following sentences. Two of the sentences are correct.

1. Whom did you see who you knew?

2. The alumni gave the party for whomever graduated before 1910.

3. The future belongs to anyone who the gods smile on.

4. Girls often make passes at boys who, contrary to popular opinion, wear glasses.

5. We don't know whom they were.

6. Doofo stopped in his tracks, because he thought he saw a train.

7. PBS which we often watch has changed its prime time schedule.

8. The Discipline Committee presented the ultimatum to whoever they felt needed the reminder.

9. A person who you don't know called while you were out.

10. Since the holiday fell on Wednesday we took Monday off.

11. Racing into the dining room the eager eater collided with the large Virginia ham on the sideboard.

12. To have one's name placed on the ballot he or she must present the nominating committee with a petition.

13. Everyone who we know is exhausted from studying grammar.

14. Grammar which is a useful tool is not an end in itself.

15. Because our economy is inflating at an astronomical rate one should make good use of his or her textbooks.

16. The typewriter collapsed, because it was getting so old.

17. Rotundo the Magnificent stopped eating Twinkies since he was becoming addicted to them.

18. Fractured the math class turned to percentage.